PYROTECHNICS

PYROTECHNICS
From the Viewpoint of Solid State Chemistry

Joseph Howard McLain

THE FRANKLIN INSTITUTE PRESS

iv

Published by THE FRANKLIN INSTITUTE PRESS^{sm}
Philadelphia, Pennsylvania.

Current printing (last digit):

5   4   3   2   1

ISBN Number: 0-89168-032-2
Library of Congress Catalog Card Number: 80-19641

Printed in the United States of America.

This book is dedicated to Ann, Elizabeth, Lynn, John, Bryson, Ann Auld, Jed and Benj whose love has meant so much to a very wonderful life.

Also to the thousands of my students whose respect I have enjoyed and hopefully earned.

Joseph H. McLain
W. Alton Jones Professor of Chemistry
and President
Washington College
Chestertown, MD

November 16, 1979

Preface

I believe in fundamental science, any scientific advancement ultimately helps. You can't view scientific pursuit as a coin-in-the-slot operation.
                                                                R. K. Narayan

The importance of pyrotechnics is so apparent to everyone in the field that it is seldom pointed out to the uninitiated. From a military aspect, pyrotechnics is the vital "horseshoe nail" of ordnance which, in turn, is vital to national defense. Civil pyrotechnics has both aesthetic and pragmatic value as exemplified by the beautiful, if fleeting, fireworks displays, and the fusee signal flare which saves lives on rail and road. The Apollo 12 spacecraft contained over two hundred pyrotechnic devices. Other applications include illuminating flares, delay trains, squibs, matches, primers, colored smokes, screening smokes, and incendiaries. These few examples merely suggest the breadth of pyrotechnics' contribution to national programs important to all of us.

Since the age of twelve, when I received a chemistry set and promptly proceeded to make assorted inks and stinks, red fire and green fire, to the suffering of my parents and the detriment of household furnishings and air purity, I have been connected in some way with pyrotechnic reactions. Fifty years later, as I write this preface, I reflect on the chain of events that has led to this moment: ill-fated attempts to prepare nitroglycerine; preparation of ritual flare mixes for fraternity activities in college; the brief but spectacular meeting of a quarter pound of sodium metal with the Chester River; days in The Hopkins listening to Dr. Robert W. Wood describe Barlow's tests of his unpronounceable and equally ineffective Glmite; service as a munitions development engineer and Chief of the Smokes Branch of the Pyrotechnics Division at the Army Chemical Center during World War II; part owner and technical director of a fireworks and munitions loading factory; and consultant on explosives, propellants, and pyrotechnics for five government installations and six commercial concerns. All during this time I have collected and savored the small triumphs of theory which have worked and regretted those which have not. Resolved always to learn more, I have tried and am still trying to make a science out of what was and still is primarily an art.

Civil pyrotechnics has been the property and livelihood of a very small group of artisans, generally of German or Italian extraction, very few of whom are trained chemists. Their formulae or recipes are literally handed down from father to son. Although glamorous enough for boys, pyrotechnics has suffered greatly by being treated as just a hobby by the trained physical chemist. The chemist finds it more professionally rewarding and physically safer to study and contribute to spectroscopy, kinetics, and similar fields. Pyrotechnics' poor-relation status was particularly true prior to World War II, and it was not until composite solid propellants of extremely high specific impulse were needed and conceived that the subject received truly scientific treatment.

There are very few books in the field and the published literature of other kinds is meager. The most recent book, *Modern Pyrotechnics* by Dr. Herbert Ellern (Chemical Publishing Co., New York, 1961, 2nd ed.), contains the following statement in its preface:

> One would expect that World War II might have brought forth at least one comprehensive treatment of modern pyrotechnics, accessible to the English speaking world. No such book has appeared in Europe or America. This is the only book of its kind in the English language.

The author also apologizes for the lack of a more scientific attitude and his necessarily empirical approach, but states that it is hard to deny that pyrotechnics is still an art rather than a science.

Published pyrotechnic material, sparse as it is, has been to a large degree a collection of formulae and recipes. This is better than nothing and serves as a starting place from which, we hope, some future scientific Olympian will deliver us from chaotic empiricism to sound theory.

One of the main reasons that pyrotechnics is still largely an art is just this lack of a literature. Publications play a vital role in the evolution of a discipline from art to science. They create a history and a basis for measuring progress. From such records, principles rather than recipes emerge.

The gods help those who help themselves, and it is my belief that many of the formulae and compositions that exist today were actually obtained on physical chemical principles, although perhaps unknowingly, and can be explained on the same basis. Such explanations, right or wrong, partial or complete, will then guide the efforts of future workers in the field so that pyrotechnics can become part of the ordered realm of chemistry.

Two analogous situations in the recent past illustrate this view. One has to do with intermetallic chemistry. Linus Pauling in *Nature of the Chemical*

Bond (Cornell University Press, Ithaca, N.Y., 1960), lamenting the lack of interest and progress in this field, said, "I think, however, that the most important reason for neglect of *this branch* of chemistry during the past century is that a theory of valence and structure for intermetallic compounds was not developed at the same time as for other compounds." The second instance occurred in transition-metal chemistry. No one will deny that interest and progress in this field had been desultory at best. Then, Leslie E. Orgel's *An Introduction to Transition-Metal Chemistry: Ligand-Field Theory* (Methuen, London, 1960) appeared to unify and give direction to this branch of chemistry. Within two years after publication of Orgel's work, contributions to journals of inorganic chemistry doubled, and, within five years, doubled again.

Pyrotechnics may become the arena for a similarly flourishing development. Approximately twenty years ago, Spice and Staveley published two articles in the open chemical literature in which they proved conclusively that the solid-solid self-propagating exothermic reactions studied by them during World War II proceeded through a preignition stage that was truly a solid-solid reaction. It was some time before I recognized the true significance of their work, but it is now obvious to me that to understand pyrotechnic reactions one must first understand the theories and principles of solid-state chemistry.

The preignition reaction (PIR) of Spice and Staveley is the first to occur in the layer just ahead of the advancing incandescent zone. Heat from the PIR, if liberated slowly enough, may gently dissipate to the surroundings, allowing the reacting material to cool. However, if the PIR produces heat faster than heat is lost, the temperature of the solid material rises. This temperature rise increases the reaction rate, which, in turn, increases the rate of heat generation, and so on. The process accelerates until either ignition occurs or the reaction is slowed down by an accumulation of solid reaction products or a decrease in the availability of reactants.

If one can control the temperature required to start the PIR, as well as the slope of the rate-vs-temperature curve, then one can control the reactivity of the system. Also, if the PIR is a true solid-state reaction, then reactivity control may be attained by solid-state methods. The theory of pyrotechnic reactions (those which can be shown to have a PIR) is, therefore, the theory of solid-state reactivity.

It is my fond hope that by applying the elements of solid state theory to a number of pyrotechnic systems, I shall help to provide a coherent basis for the science of pyrotechnics.

I should like to mention the many people who have influenced me in this area. Mr. Frank L. LaMotte, Prof. J.C.W. Frazer, Dr. O.G. Bennett, Col. Ralph W. Hufferd, Dr. H.C. Clauser, Mr. Roland Meekins, Mr. George Veneroso, Mr. Warren Thrasher, Dr. Tenney L. Davis, Mr. Anthony P. Fabrizi, Mr. Wilbur Lizza, Dr. D. Hart, Prof. Dr. J. Arvid Hedvall, Mr. Gunther Cohn, Mr. Victor G. Willis, Prof. Dr. G.-M. Schwab, and Mr. M. Vara-darajan are some whom I remember gratefully for imparting information and inspiration along a tortuous but fascinating road.

It would be manifestly unfair not to mention and thank the hundreds of students at Washington College and the Franklin Institute who have con-tributed. This book is an outgrowth of lectures given for more than twelve years at these institutions and abroad.

A very special thanks and much credit must go to Dr. John A. Conkling who has written parts of two chapters, Fireworks and Analysis, not just for these contributions but for the encouragement he has given me as one of my students, as a colleague in the Chemistry Department, and as the legitimate heir to the aspiration of making pyrotechnics the science it should come to be.

Thanks also to Mrs. Jean Keene for her patience and encouragement, and for her skill and diligence in typing the manuscript.

AGNI   KALA

अग्नि कला

Joseph H. McLain
W. Alton Jones Professor of
        Chemistry
Washington College
Chestertown, Maryland

CONTENTS

Chapter I

BACKGROUND FOR PYROTECHNIC THEORY

It is certainly not the least charm of a theory that it is refutable.
F.W. Nietzche

The thrust of this work is pyrotechnics and the application of those solid-state chemistry principles pertinent to pyrotechnic problems. Books are already available which give an excellent treatment of solid-state chemistry; we will make no attempt here to present another authoritative treatise on that large and complex subject. Consequently, all examples discussed involve only pyrotechnic systems.

Moreover, this is not a "how to" book as such. For example, it includes almost no package design. It does include formulae, equations, and chemical principles, but these are generally presented and used, not derived or proved.

Theory is a much abused concept. It is a commonplace to equate *theoretical* with *impractical*. The often loudly voiced complaint that someone is "too theoretical" arises when theory is misused as a synonym for hypothesis or opinion, usually in regard to sociological, educational, or economic concerns. The social sciences lack the sample uniformity and size generally available to the natural sciences. Furthermore, the reactions of human beings to given constraints or perturbations are not a fixed function independent of time, whereas chloride ions react with silver ions to form a slightly soluble silver chloride yesterday, today and tomorrow.

1

THEORY VS. EMPIRICISM

Although the trial-and-error method is sometimes unavoidable, and often works, sound theory properly applied is the most practical approach to the solution of chemical problems. For example, a pyrotechnic delay is required with a burning rate of 2.00 ± 0.20 cm/sec at ambient temperatures between $-40\,°C$ and $75\,°C$. The material must be easily ignitable from primer flash and meet certain other criteria. Is it feasible to test all combinations of metal reducing agents and solid oxidants?

Assuming only 67 reductants and some 60 oxidants, there would be 4020 binary mixes and about 250,000 ternary mixes. Even if one mix could be evaluated each week, it would take 80 years for the binaries and more than 5,000 years for the ternaries. Without some theory, the task would be Herculean.

Another example of applied theory involves the gaseous products of the reactions between S and $KClO_3$. It is desirable to control the rate of this reaction for dissemination of aerosols. It could be assumed that the reaction proceeds by means of a decomposition mechanism such as:

$$2KClO_3 \rightarrow KClO_4 + KCl + O_2 \text{ or } 2KCl + 3O_2$$
$$O_2 + S \rightarrow SO_2 + heat$$

If this is indeed the case, then addition of a decomposition catalyst such as MnO_2 should speed up the reaction. However, thermal analysis showed that the reaction proceeds at a much lower temperature than is characteristic of decomposition, and the addition of MnO_2 to the reaction mixture had no measurable effect. This led to a hypothesis that the controlling factor was the *looseness* of the $KClO_3$ crystal. Later work confirmed this[1]. (See Chapter IV on crystal *looseness*.)

PRE-THEORETICAL HYPOTHESES

Hypotheses are the bases for theory. Although this sounds obvious, it is a necessary and profound statement. Without a hypothesis, data have little shape, and experiment design lacks the basis for direction. Too many times, problems are attacked by inundation rather than by directed effort. To know where to go, you need a starting place and a goal. The route may have to be changed during progress toward that goal, but there should always be a point of reference.

We encountered one example of this use of hypothesis in early work on "gasless" delay compositions. Our most serious problem was failure of the reaction to propagate through the entire length of the column. It soon became apparent that this problem was most severe with small column diameters, in metal tubes, and at low temperatures. These factors all promoted rapid heat loss. We hypothesized that the burning was a series of reignitions along the length of the delay column from layer to layer of the compressed mixture. If so, the most effective delay composition should be one with the highest ratio of heat reaction ΔH_R, to ignition temperature, T_{ign}. This fraction was called the propagation index, P_I:

$$P_I = \frac{\Delta H_R}{T_{ign}}$$

and used with much success. Subsequent work by Rose[2] extended and confirmed this hypothesis.

BASIS OF PRESENT THEORY

The basis for the theory of pyrotechnic reactions derives largely from a paper by Spice and Staveley[3]. A summary of their work follows.

Although they dealt with two systems of self-propagating incandescent reactants:

$$K_2Cr_2O_7 + 2Fe \rightarrow Fe_2O_3 + Cr_2O_3 + K_2O$$
$$3BaO_2 + 2Fe \rightarrow Fe_2O_3 + 3BaO$$

most of their diagnostic work was confined to the $Fe-BaO_2$ mixture. They dry-mixed the two reactant powders, compressed the mix into pellets, sealed the pellets into glass vessels, and placed the vessels in a heating chamber for various periods of time. Reaction progress was determined in situ by quantitative measurement of the disappearance of the magnetic elemental Fe.

The PIR

This study proved that two reactions were occurring: ignition and preignition. The preignition reaction (PIR) yielded the products shown in the second of the above equations.

Three possible mechanisms for this reaction suggest themselves:

1. $2BaO_2 + heat \rightarrow 2BaO + O_2$ (gas), in which the gaseous O_2 then attacks the Fe.
2. $BaO_2 + heat \rightarrow BaO_2$ (liquid), in which the liquid BaO_2 attacks the Fe.
3. A genuine solid-solid reaction with no gaseous or liquid phase.

The authors eliminated possibilities 1 and 2 on the following grounds:

(a) If a gas is involved, the rate-determining step would be O_2 diffusion through the Fe_2O_3 layer to metallic Fe. However, kinetic experiments with Fe and gaseous O_2 demonstrated that activation energies for this reaction were very different from that of the PIR in a compacted powder.

(b) BaO_2 kept at 335 °C (PIR temperature) for hours showed no measurable dissociation pressure or reduction in BaO_2 content.

(c) When one pellet of pure Fe and one of BaO_2 were sealed in opposite ends of an evacuated U-tube, and the tube was heated for four hours at 335 °C, neither pellet changed weight.

(d) Addition of Fe_2O_3 (a known catalyst for the decomposition of BaO_2) to the BaO_2-Fe mix decreased the PIR rate.

(e) An increase in the pressure used to form the pellets (with a consequent increase in packing density) increased the PIR rate. This is opposite to what one would expect if gases were diffusing within the pellets, but just what one would expect if crystal lattice units were diffusing.

(f) Pellets heated during continuous evacuation showed no decrease in the PIR rate and, in some instances, the rate actually increased. Neither of these results would occur if gaseous diffusion were involved.

(g) The liquid state cannot be involved because Fe has much too high a melting point and, although BaO_2 melts at 400 °C (closer to the PIR temperature, but still some 65 °C above it), there was no evidence of melting at any time. Furthermore, a PIR was observed with the Fe-$K_2Cr_2O_7$ mixture at temperatures more than 100 °C below the $K_2Cr_2O_7$ melting point.

By elimination, then, the authors concluded that the PIR is a genuine solid-solid reaction. Indeed, the solid-solid mechanism explains the rate increase with increased packing density in terms of increased contact surface between particles, and explains the rate decrease with addition of Fe_2O_3 in terms of the oxide's action as an inert diluent similar to kaolin, superfloss, and other materials used for many years to retard burning rates in delay systems. It should be mentioned here that these effects of compaction and inert dilution are useful for determining if some other pyrotechnic system is also a solid-solid reaction.

If the PIR is the necessary precursor to the bulk, incandescent, self-propagating reaction, it must then play an important role in the initiation of that reaction (reactivity). Thus, if one can control the onset of the PIR and the slope of its self-heating curve, one can control the bulk reaction. Because the PIR is a true solid-solid reaction, the control method lies in the principles of solid-state chemistry.

Low-energy reactions

Unfortunately, little of the abundant literature on solid-state chemistry applies directly to the PIR. Although much has been published on the reactivity of solids since the classical introductory work of G. Tammann[4], most efforts have remained surprisingly confined to systems of the same relatively low-energy type investigated by Tammann and his students, i.e., systems in which heats of reaction are almost always well under 100 cal/g. Typical of these reactions are:

$$PbS + CdO \rightarrow PbO + CdS$$
$$ZnS + PbO \rightarrow PbS + ZnO$$
$$CuSO_4 + CaO \rightarrow CaSO_4 + CuO$$
$$BaO + ZnSO_4 \rightarrow BaSO_4 + ZnO$$

The most recent books in this field[5,6] contain no reference to high energy reactions and Garner[7] gives only one:

$$Mg + ZnS \rightarrow MgS + Zn$$

which has a heat of reaction of 300 cal/g.

NEED FOR HIGH ENERGY THEORY

Many higher-energy systems, although of practical importance, have been virtually neglected, presumably due to a belief that they are not truly solid-solid but may involve a liquid phase. Theory also lagged, even after Spice and Staveley[8] proved that reactions of Fe with BaO_2 or $K_2Cr_2O_7$ are indeed solid-solid and have a PIR. Some practical applications of higher-energy systems are as follows:

One of the most intriguing is as fillers for delay trains. For example, a PbO-Si mixture has provided a delay of 1.25 to 1.75 sec/in between the primer flash and final detonation of a grenade. A PbO_2-Si mixture is used as a delay in blasting caps[9]. The literature describes some 80 such delay mixtures, with burning rates ranging from milliseconds to 40 sec/in, but says little about underlying theory. We will deal more specifically with delays in Chapter V.

CaSi$_2$ mixed with Fe$_3$O$_4$ supplied the heat for self-heating food cans in World War II[10]. Other "gasless" heating mixtures have contained Zn, BaCrO$_4$, and MnO$_2$. The Goldschmidt reaction:

$$8Al \text{ (solid)} + 3Fe_3O_4 \text{ (solid)} \rightarrow 4Al_2O_3 \text{ (solid)} + 9Fe \text{ (liquid)}$$

probably the oldest of this type, has been used for almost a century to produce molten iron *in situ* for repairing cast iron equipment.

Other mixes that have been used to synthesize metals include:

$$4BaO + 2Al \rightarrow 3Ba + BaO \cdot Al_2O_3$$
$$3TiO_2 + 4Al \rightarrow 3Ti + 2Al_2O_3$$

A solid mixture of ZnO, Al, and C$_2$Cl$_6$ produces a smoke screen for troop protection.

Zr-BaCrO$_4$ mixtures have supplied heat to trigger special batteries.

Mixtures of PbO and Si (or B) have been used as normally open electric switches. In the reaction:

$$2PbO + Si \rightarrow SiO_2 + 2Pb$$

the reactants are poor electric conductors, but the metallic product conducts well and closes the circuit.

Conversely, mixtures such as Fe-BaO$_2$ make normally closed electric switches. In the reaction:

$$Fe + 3BaO_2 \rightarrow Fe_2O_3 + 3BaO$$

the reactant mixture is a good conductor because of its metal content, but initiation and burning convert it into insulating oxides and open the electric circuit.

Because of the importance of these reactions, the shortcomings of the literature are all the more regrettable. The classical imaginative work of Spice and Staveley established the connection between pyrotechnics and solid-state chemistry; it remains now to build on this foundation and to advance the theory and art of pyrotechnics.

A scientific investigator needs a theory much as a speleologist needs a string when exploring a new cave. Without such a reference to guide the way, the investigator tends to get lost in a sea of data and to lose sight of the goal. As Dr. Milton Eisenhower said of a former U.S. president, "You must have a deep-seated philosophy to guide you. In the White House when you're making twenty fateful decisions a day, you'd better have a philosophy to keep you straight." Research chemists call it a theory or hypothesis, rather than a philosophy, and it must rest on proven principles and true observations. Only then can the researcher devise appropriate experiments to confirm or deny the theory. Only then can he or she be "kept straight,"

> *For out of old feldes, as men seyth,*
> *Cometh al this newe corn from yer to yere;*
> *And out of olde bokes, in good feyth,*
> *Cometh al this newe science that men lere.*

Geoffrey Chaucer

Chapter I

REFERENCES

1. McLain, J.H. and McClure, M.D., *Effect of Phase Change in Solid-Solid Reactions*, Report WCDC 6667, Grant DA-AMC-18-035-77(A), Chemical Research and Development Laboratories, Edgewood Arsenal, Md., 1967.
2. *Flame Propagation Parameters of Pyrotechnic Delay and Ignition Compositions*, IHMR 71-168, Department of the Navy, Indian Head, Md., 1971.
3. Spice, J.E. and Staveley, L.A.K., *J. Soc. Chem. Ind.* **68**, 313-319 (1949).
4 Tammann, G., *Zeit. f. anorg. Chem.* **149**, 21-98 (1925).
5. Hannay, N.B., *Solid State Chemistry*, Prentice-Hall, Englewood Cliffs, N.J., 1967.
6. Galwey, A.K., *Chemistry of Solids*, Chapman and Hall, London, 1967.
7. Garner, W.E., Ed., *Chemistry of the Solid State*, Butterworth, London, 1955 (available from University Microfilms, Ann Arbor, Mich.).
8. Spice, J.E. and Staveley, L.A.K., *J. Soc. Chem. Ind.* **68**, 348 (1949).
9. McLain, Joseph H., *Pyrotechnics and Solid State Chemistry*, Lecture Notes, Franklin Institute, 1978.
10. Taylor, J., *Solid Propellant and Exothermic Compositions*, George Newnes, London, 1959.

Chapter II

THE SOLID STATE

Textbooks and Heaven only are Ideal
Solidity is an imperfect state
Within the cracked and dislocated Real
Nonstoichiometric crystals dominate.
John Updike, *The Dance of the Solids*

Why is there a solid-state chemistry at all? We have physical chemistry, organic and inorganic, but we do not have gas or liquid chemistry. Solid, liquid, and gas are only physical states, often transient, that change with temperature. Whether phenol is a liquid or a solid may depend on the local climate and the time of the year. What makes the solid state so unique that we treat it as a separate realm?

The uniqueness of the solid state lies in the fact that while the chemical reactivity of liquids and gases depends on bulk properties, the reactivity of solids depends on departures from bulk properties. This difference stems from the fundamental nature of solids.

When two particles are placed in intimate contact, something must cross the boundary for a reaction to occur; there must be something to diffuse out and some place to diffuse to. Obviously, if the cohesive structure of each particle were perfect, nothing would be free to move and there would be no openings for it to move into, so no reaction would take place. Imperfections, often very small, in the solid structure make reactions possible and are all important in determining reactivity between solids. In some solid-solid reactions, it is not even the proverbial tail that wags the dog; it is the fleas on the end of the tail!

9

HISTORICAL BACKGROUND

The infamous doctrine, *Corpora non agunt nisi fluida* ("Bodies do not act unless in the fluid state"), attributed to Aristotle, ruled chemical thought until well into the twentieth century. The first conclusive proof that solids can and will react by themselves was the making a ceramic pigment, Rinman's Green, by Hedvall[1] in 1912. He mixed and heated black Co_3O_4 and white ZnO and observed that small green crystals formed between 500°C and 900°C, temperatures at which neither the liquid nor the vapor phase could conceivably play a role. Important work by G. Tammann and his students followed. Yet Desch could still state in his presidential address to the Royal Society in 1925, "It is remarkable how little we know about the chemical properties of solids."

Although the solid-state chemistry literature is now fairly large, most of it has appeared since 1946. Important exceptions are works by Hedvall, C. Wagner. G.-M. Schwab, Huttig, and Hauffe. Not until the discovery of solid-state electronics and the physicists' interest in and development of semiconductors did progress in solid-state chemistry begin with genuine zeal.

In the past thirty years, this previously neglected field has begun to flourish. The excellent reference work by Garner et al (cited in Chapter I) has been and still is invaluable in summarizing achieved knowledge, promoting order, and stimulating further efforts.

In retrospect, the lateness of this development is hard to understand. After all, solids have three dimensions. They are made into common objects such as bridges, buildings, automobiles, and airplanes. They can be thrown or stumbled over, touched and felt, and above all, unlike most gases, they can be seen. Thus, to a layman, a theory of solids would logically precede a theory of gases.

This might be true if we did not make the necessary distinction between objects and substances. Early astronomers knew a great deal about the motions of planets, and physicists knew the paths of projectiles and the laws of falling bodies. However, chemists are concerned more with the substances that comprise these objects than with the objects themselves. We have had a Stone Age, a Bronze Age, and an Iron Age; we now have an Atomic Age, the very name of which indicates our interest in the structure and properties of substances.

The late development of solid-state chemistry is also surprising in that some of the oldest processes known to man involve the reactions of solids. The making of ceramics, for one, started in the days of the cave dwellers and was developed by the ancient Egyptians to a high degree of sophistication in fabrication, heat treatment, and decoration. The manufacture of bronze weapons demanded the skills of alloying, heat treatment, and work harden-ing. Production of gun powder needed the technologies of mixing and grain-ing as did the making of all other pyrotechnics developed by ancient civiliza-tions. Limestone was quarried, carved, and calcined centuries before Christ. Lapidaries plied their arts all over the world, polishing and cutting gem stones. Why then did the essential nature of the solid state remain hidden?

The Aristotelian doctrine undoubtedly had a deterring effect, but this was certainly aided by the impatience of chemists. Although we now know that solids can react, we also know that the rates of solid-solid reactions are exponentially slower than those of either the gaseous or liquid phase. To chemists or alchemists who lacked this knowledge, it seemed only practical to carry out most reactions in solution or by heating one or more reactants to the melting point.

Probably, too, the unquestioned success of the theory of perfect or ideal gases, the solid counterpart of which is the perfect crystal, caused some of the myopia. It took a long time for scientists to realize that few, if any, crystals are perfect at any temperature, and that no crystal is perfect at temperatures greater than 20 °K. Thus, although the behavior of real gases can be quite successfully extrapolated from the behavior of ideal gases, the relation be-tween real and perfect crystals is more complex. Reactivity, tensile strength, elasticity, malleability, and thermal and electrical conductivity are all influenced by the type and extent of imperfections in the solids.

CRYSTALS

Most solids are or can be crystalline. A crystal is a homogeneous structure in which constituent atoms are arranged in a regular repeated pattern. The plane geometric figures displayed by crystal surfaces are evidence of internal order. The smallest repeated unit, or building block, of the crystal is called the unit cell, and the orderly array of points in space with which the atom groups can be associated is called the crystal lattice. (Some solids are amorphous, i.e., non-crystalline. Examples are charcoal, asphalt, waxes, and glass. Because their somewhat chaotic physical arrangement of atoms resembles that of a liquid frozen rigid before it had a chance to crystallize, these mate-rials are often called supercooled liquids.)

Chemical bonds

Crystalline solids are generally categorized according to the chemical bond that holds the crystal together. In their usual descending order of strength, the bonds are covalent, ionic, metallic, hydrogen (bridge), and Van der Waals' (intermolecular).

In *covalent* crystals, such as diamond, silicon, gray tin, and graphite, atoms are held together by electron-pair bonds.

In *ionic* crystals, such as alkali metal halides and metallic oxides and hydroxides, a large difference in electronegativity between constituents produces attraction between their unlike electric charges.

In *metallic* crystals, such as the elemental metals, electrons are shared broadly without preferential directions defined by atom pairs.

Intermolecular crystals, such as sucrose, phenol, and naphthalene, are held together by *van der Waals'* forces between molecules, the weakest bond of all, and sometimes by *hydrogen* bonding between the hydrogen atom of one molecule and two unshared electrons of another.

A list of chemical bonds gives an oversimplified view of the cohesiveness of solids. For example, many crystals are simultaneously ionic and covalent in varying degrees. Pauling[2] discusses bonds in greater detail.

Physical properties

The physical properties of solids depend greatly on the crystal bonding forces. Diamond and carborundum are very hard partly because the covalent bond in their crystals is very strong. Melting points tend to be higher for crystals with stronger bonds because their atoms are more difficult to separate. Metals are generally more malleable and ductile than other solids because their bonding forces have little or no preferred orientation. Thus, the assembly of atoms tolerates deformation without bond rupture.

Properties of solids also depend on the specific crystal structure since the same atoms may link together in several different possible configurations. Diamond and graphite are both composed solely of carbon atoms, yet one is hard and the other is soft. The reason is that in diamond the carbon atoms are packed closely together. This increases the forces between them and prevents easy displacement by external pressures. In graphite, the carbon atoms are more loosely organized.

Crystal structures are characterized by the geometric symmetries of the unit cell repeated throughout the lattice, and sometimes by the closeness of the packing. Pauling described Barlow's work[3] on cubic and hexagonal close packing as "the problem of packing spheres in ways that leave a minimum of interstitial space." This concept is sometimes called the *Law of Conservation of Space*. Empirical tests have shown that spheres naturally assemble in only two ways, with either cubic or hexagonal symmetry. Metal crystals, which tend to grow by the accumulation of single-size spherical molecules, display these two symmetries. Other crystals grow from molecules of different shapes.

Plate-like molecules stack somewhat like dishes; stick-like molecules pack side by side; and pear-shaped molecules cluster in various configurations, all generally in accordance with the principle of space conservation.

CRYSTAL DEFECTS

The relation between physical properties of the solid and the chemical and geometric crystal classification is far from exact because solids are not single, perfect crystals. A solid body may be composed of grains, or small crystals (themselves imperfect), joined at boundaries that form discontinuities in the structure. Defects may be relatively gross, even visible to the unaided eye or under the microscope, or relatively small, on the atomic level. Both can have profound effects on physical and chemical properties.

For example, ionic bonds as evidenced by laboratory experience with a mortar and pestle do not seem to be all that strong. The weakness is due to crystal defects. Thus, because of imperfections, the experimental tensile strength of sodium chloride crystal is hundreds of times less than its theoretical value.

Moelwyn-Hughes[4] points out evidence for the existence of defects in the form of discrepancies in Avogadro's number as determined from the equation:

$$N = \frac{ZM}{V\rho}$$

where N is Avogadro's number, Z is the number of molecules or ion pairs per unit cell, M is the gram formula weight, V is the unit-cell volume in cm^3, and ρ is the crystal density in g/cm^3. The number obtained varies and is usually higher than dependable values derived from other sources. Since the variables in the equation are measurable to an accuracy of 0.01%, discrepancies of the order of 1% may be considered real. The conclusion is that the true density of the crystals is less than the theoretical density. Moelwyn-Hughes attributes this to some unoccupied lattice sites (see *Lattice defects* below). This is probably only part of the explanation; it is likely that jogs, cracks, and dislocations (see *Dislocations* below) also contribute to the reduction of density.

Calculations of this type for nine alkali halides[5], summarized in Table 1, indicate the extent of the discrepancy between real and ideal densities. Z for all cubic alkali halide crystals is 4.00. The accepted value of Avogadro's number is 6.022 x 10^{23} mol^{-1}.

Table I. Apparent discrepancies in Avogadro's number

	KCl	KBr	KI	LiCl	LiBr	LiI	NaCl	NaBr	NaI
Unit cell side, 10^{-3} cm	6.28	6.58	7.06	5.14	5.50	6.04	5.62	5.96	6.46
Unit cell vol., 10^{-24} cm^3	247.8	284.9	351.9	135.8	166.4	220.3	117.5	211.7	269.6
Gram formula wt., g	74.55	119.01	166.02	42.40	86.86	133.86	58.45	102.91	149.92
Density, g/cm^3	1.984	2.75	3.13	2.068	3.464	4.061	2.165	3.203	3.667
Calculated N, 10^{23} x	6.069	6.076	6.029	6.039	6.029	5.984	6.084	6.070	6.066
Discrepancy, %	+0.8	+0.9	+0.1	+0.3	+0.1	−0.6	+1.0	+0.8	+0.7

The greatest discrepancy is approximately 1%, for NaCl, and the smallest is 0.1%. Note that the calculated Avogrado's number for LiI, contrary to the others, indicates a real density higher than the theoretical value. Although part of the discrepancy may be due to experimental error, the direction of the discrepancy might be expected from the great difference between the ionic radii of Li$^+$ (0.60 x 10^{-8} cm) and I$^-$ (2.16 x 10^{-8} cm). The ratio of 3.6 between radii is equivalent to a ratio of about 47 between the volumes of the ions. A combination of large and small ions allows compact packing and a relatively high density.

Dislocations, cracks, and jogs

A crystal may contain structural dislocations along certain lines that run between grain boundaries or other dislocations. These may form as the growing crystal acquires more molecules that do not fit properly into the normal pattern. The faults do not heal with continued overgrowth.

Some faults may be due to the acquisition of alien constituents, i.e., impurities. Impurities that occupy sites for which they are too large or too small, compared with the normal occupants, may generate a defect that will propagate through the crystal like a run in a nylon stocking.

Smekal[6] has discussed cracks and jogs in the crystal structure that contribute to the chemical reactivity of solids. At crystal decomposition temperatures, material is lost first at edges or corners. Reaction of a liquid with a crystal begins at defects where bonds are weakened. Rates of adsorption, decomposition, and solution increase with greater surface area. Smekal cracks and jogs make a solid more reactive by creating a larger number of edges and corners and by exposing more crystal surface. Dislocations have a similar effect.

Lattice defects

Inherent defects. Inherent defects were first proposed by Frenkel[7] and

Schottky[8]. These are the absences or displacements of atoms from their normal lattice sites and do not involve the intrusion of impurities. They are shown schematically in Figure 1.

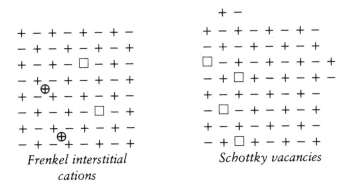

*Frenkel interstitial
cations*   *Schottky vacancies*

Figure 1. *Inherent crystal defects*

Any stoichiometric crystal in thermal equilibrium above about $10\,°K$ necessarily contains Frenkel and Schottky defects. Although energy is expended in defect formation, the defective crystal becomes more stable thermodynamically because of a proportionately compensating increase in configurational entropy.

Impurity defects. Disorders in the lattice may also be due to the presence of alien atoms that do not fit as well as normal constituents. We must therefore be concerned about purity if we are to understand the behavior of the substance.

What do we mean by the question, "Is it pure?" Did purity mean the same thing to Lavoisier, Priestley, or Arrhenius as it does to us today? Probably, a more revealing question is, "How pure is it?"

Consider the ionic solid NaCl, 58.44 g of which contains $2 \times 6.022 \times 10^{23} = 1.204 \times 10^{24}$ ions, and which has a density of $2.165\ g/cm^3$. One gram formula weight would occupy about $27\ cm^3$, and $1\ cm^3$ would contain $1.204 \times 10^{24}/27 = 4.46 \times 10^{22}$ ions. Let us suppose that after many recrystallizations we are able to obtain a 1-cm^3 crystal which is 99.9999% pure. This very rare and costly crystal of NaCl would still contain 4.46×10^{16} impurities. Even a microscopic cube of this highly purified substance, 1 μm on an edge, would contain more than 40,000 impurities. How pure one considers this to be depends on one's frame of reference. The nature and number of these impurities significantly affect the chemical and physical properties of the crystal.

Nonstoichiometric defects. It is well known that many chemical compounds deviate from stoichiometry. Some examples are ZnO, NiO, Cu_2O, Fe_3O_4, PbO_2, Pb_3O_4, and $CaSi_2$. Such deviations are associated with lattice defects. For example, an AB crystal may have vacancies of the A species but not of the B. Alternatively, a lattice may preferentially accept one species into interstitial sites.

If these are ionic crystals, they must remain electrically neutral. Thus, if a crystal of a given compound has an excess of interstitial cations, it must also have an equal excess of trapped electrons. Nonstoichiometry must therefore affect the electronic properties of the crystal.

The four known types of nonstoichiometric crystals are pictured in Figure 2.

```
Me+  X-  Me+  X-  Me+  X-              Me+  X-  Me+  X-  Me+  X-
X-  Me+  [e]  Me+  X-  Me+            X-  Me+  X-  Me+  X-  Me+
Me+  X-  Me+  X-  Me+  X-                      Me+e
X-  Me+  X-  Me+  [ ]  Me+            Me+  X-  Me+  X-  Me+  X-
Me+  X-  Me+  X-  Me+  X-              X-  Me+  X-  Me+  X-  Me+
X-  Me+  X-  Me+  X-  Me+             Me+  X-  Me+  X-  Me+  X-
                                              Me+e
                                      X-  Me+  X-  Me+  X-  Me+
```

Type I	Type II
Excess of metal due to anion vacancies	*Excess of metal due to interstitial cations.*

```
Me+  X-  Me+  X-  Me+  X-  Me+  X-      Me+  X-  Me+  X-  Me+  X-  Me+  X-
X-  Me+  X-  Me+  X-  Me+ X- Me+        X-  Me+  X-  [ ]  X-  Me+  X-  Me+
                            X-
Me+  X-  Me+  X-  Me++ X-  Me+  X-      Me+  X-  Me++ X-  Me+  X-  Me+  X-
X-  Me+  X-  Me+  X-  Me+  X-  Me+      X-  Me+  X-  Me+  X-  Me+  X-  Me+
Me+  X-  Me+ X-  Me+  X-  Me+  X-       Me+  X-  Me+  X-  [ ]  X-  Me++ X-
          X-
X-  Me++ X-  Me+  X-  Me+  X-  Me+      X-  Me+  X-  Me+  X-  Me+  X-  Me+
Me+  X-  Me+  X-  Me+  X-  Me+  X-      Me+  X-  Me+  X-  Me+  X-  Me+  X-
X-  Me+  X-  Me+  X-  Me+  X-  Me+      X-  Me+  X-  Me+  X-  Me+  X-  Me+
```

Type III	Type IV
Excess of anion due to interstitial anions.	*Excess of anion due to cation vacancies.*

Figure 2. *Nonstoichiometric crystal defects*

SEMICONDUCTORS

These nonstoichiometric crystals may be further classified into two semiconductor categories: types I and II are termed *n*-type semiconductors, and types III and IV are termed *p*-type semiconductors. The meanings of these names can best be defined by a discussion of elementary intrinsic semiconductors.

First of all, what is semiconductivity? Primarily, semiconductors are substances that have electrical resistivities between about 10^{-3} and 10^9 ohm-cm (the limits are not sharply defined), occupying the middle ground between insulators (nonconductors) and conductors. Semiconductors also differ from metallic conductors in the dependence of resistivity on temperature. When a metallic conductor is heated, its resistivity increases (conductivity decreases); when a semiconductor is heated, its resistivity decreases (conductivity increases). The reason can be seen from the diagram in Figure 3 of a silicon crystal, a well-known intrinsic semiconductor.

Si	Si	Si	Si		Si	Si	Si	Si		Si	Si	Si	Si
Si	Si	Si	Si		Si	Si	As	Si		Si	Si	Al	Si
Si	Si	Si	Si		Si	Si	Si	Si		Si	Si	Si	Si
	a					b					c		

Figure 3. *Silicon crystal:* **a.** *pure;* **b.** *arsenic impurity;* **c.** *aluminum impurity*

If the crystal were perfect, as in Figure 3a, all of the silicon's electrons would be used for bonding and none would have the mobility necessary for conduction. However, the crystal is not perfect. Not only are there defect sites, but heating the crystal gives more vibrational freedom and mobility to its carrier electrons. However, heating is not the only or the most desirable way to increase the conductivity of semiconductors.

If we adulterate the crystal by introducing an alien atom such as arsenic or antimony into its lattice, it will appear as in Figure 3b. Arsenic has five electrons in its valence shell but only four nearest neighbors with which to share them. The extra electron cannot be a bonding electron and therefore has much higher mobility and is a better current carrier. Such adulteration is called doping and a crystal doped in this way is said to be *n*-doped (*n* for the negative charge on the mobile electron).

If, however, the dopant was an atom such as aluminum with only three electrons in its valence shell, the crystal would look as in Figure 3c. Now there are not enough electrons to complete the covalent pair. This silicon conducts by means of positive holes and is said to be p-doped. It should be emphasized that both types of doping increase the conductivity.

The classification of nonstoichometrics as n-types (I and II) and p-types (III and IV) describes the means of current carrying and is very important in chemical applications. Furthermore, both carrier types may be doped to alter their conductivity. Doping n-type nonstoichiometrics with foreign ions of higher ionic charge decreases the conductivity. Doping with ions of lower charge increases the conductivity. Just the opposite is true of p-type nonstoichiometrics. Thus, semiconductor properties depend not only on the extent of the impurity but also on its chemical identity.

Before leaving the subject of nonstoichiometrics, we should cite the work of A. D. Wadsley[9]. His crystallographic investigations showed conclusively that compounds such as Nb_2O_5, formerly considered to be nonstoichiometric with a wide homogeneity range, are really stoichiometric but to a much different degree than previously thought. For example, the system Nb_2O_5-WO_3 can give eight different compounds:

$$WNb_{68}O_{173}$$
$$WNb_{12}O_{33}$$
$$W_3Nb_{14}O_{44}$$
$$W_5Nb_{16}O_{55}$$
$$W_8Nb_{18}O_{69}$$
$$W_4Nb_{26}O_{77}$$
$$WNb_{40}O_{103}$$
$$WNb_{26}O_{68}$$

depending upon the method and temperature of preparation and crystallographic shear stress. The different atomic ratios derive from different sharings of the constituent octahedra between points, edges, or faces.

Thus we see that solids do react with solids and the reactivity derives only partially from chemical constitution, binding forces, and crystal structure. Defects, whether large or small, intrinsic or due to the intrusion of foreign ingredients, exert a strong influence on physical and chemical properties.

> *A Schottky vacancy or Frenkel interstitial,*
> *Participation is real, not artificial.*
> *Defect or hole,*
> *They play a role*
> *On the surface that's not superficial.*

can migrate through the ionic product layer only as ions, electrons must also accompany the ionic migration. Reaction will not take place if the product layer is not capable of conducting the electrons.

C. Wagner identified migrants and directions of movement with a brilliant experiment[1] involving Ag and S separated by two Ag_2S (α form) pellets as pictured schematically in Figure 1. He held the system at 220 °C for one hour after which he found that the weight of the upper Ag_2S pellet had increased by an amount stoichiometrically equivalent to a weight loss found in the Ag. The weight of the lower Ag_2S pellet remained unchanged.

This proved that Ag^+ migrates through the Ag_2S lattice and that reaction takes place only at the Ag_2S-S interface, accompanied by a reverse movement of electrons. It is not surprising that the smaller cation, Ag^+, is the more mobile species, particularly since S consists largely of S_2 and S_3 fragments at 220 °C.

Wagner also investigated the reaction:

$$Cu + AgCl \rightarrow CuCl + Ag$$

with the experimental setup of Figure 2. He proved that Cu^+ diffuses through the CuCl lattice to the CuCl-AgCl junction where it acquires an electron and forms new CuCl. Simultaneously, the Ag^+ ion moves through the AgCl lattice to the AgCl-Ag interface where it acquires an electron and forms new metal. Electrons move clockwise and ions counterclockwise.

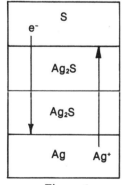

Figure 1

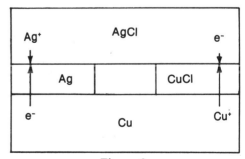

Figure 2

Ionic migration in solid-solid reactions.

SELF-PROPAGATING, INCANDESCENT, SOLID-STATE REACTIONS

Perhaps the oldest example of this type is the Goldschmidt or thermite reaction:

$$3Fe_3O_4 + 8Al \rightarrow 4Al_2O_3 + 9Fe$$

which is still used in ordnance elements and for repairing castings in the field.

Spice and Staveley worked with the following systems:

Reducing Agent	Oxidizer
Fe	BaO_2
Mn	$K_2Cr_2O_7$
Mo	$KMnO_4$
Si	$Ba(NO_3)_2$
S	$Pb(NO_3)_2$
S	$Sr(NO_3)_2$
S	KNO_3

although not in all combinations.

The author has explored many combinations of the following systems:

Reducing Agent	Oxidizer	
Si	Fe_2O_3	$Pb_2(OH)_2CrO_4$
Fe	PbO	$BaCrO_4$
Mn	Pb_3O_4	$K_2Cr_2O_7$
Zr	PbO_2	
Al	$PbCrO_4$	
S	$KMnO_4$	
Ti	NH_4ClO_4	
W	$KClO_4$	
B	$KClO_3$	
Se	Fe_3O_4	
Sn	KNO_3	
Mg	NiO	
Mo	Bi_2O_3	

Rates of reaction vary with ingredients and percentage composition from very slow (20 sec/cm) in loaded tubes to almost instantaneous. In loose powder form, PbO + Si will glow and creep, whereas Pb_3O_4 + Ti will explode audibly.

Some of the slower burning systems offer unique opportunities to study the propagation of combustion waves. The reactions are reproducible, and long-range diffusion and convection effects are generally negligible. However, variations in particle size, internal and external surface area, degree of homogeneity of the mix, and previous chemical history of oxidizers and reducers sometimes counterbalance these other advantages.

A unique characteristic of solid-solid reactions is their virtually total dependence on enthalpy. The condition for spontaneity of a reaction as demanded by the second law of thermodynamics, $\Delta G = \Delta H - T\Delta S$, is that ΔG be negative, where G is the Gibbs energy, H the enthalpy, T the absolute temperature, and S the entropy. The entropy change for reactants yielding solid products approaches zero, and Kopp's Rule states that the sum of the ionic specific heats remains unchanged. Thus, the only way ΔG can be negative is for ΔH to be negative. That is, the reaction must be exothermic. This uniqueness is also relevant to the rates of these reactions, as seen in the following discussion of the analogy with semiconductor behavior[2].

SEMICONDUCTOR ANALOGY

An oxidation-reduction reaction necessitates the transfer of electrons and can usefully be compared with semiconductor activity. The reducing agent is the electron donor and the oxidizing agent is the electron acceptor. This is analogous to the activity at an np semiconductor junction where the n-type crystal creates the space charge potential by donating electrons to the p-type crystal. Therefore, an n-type reducing agent should be more reactive than a p-type, and a p-type oxidizing agent should be more reactive than an n-type.

Schwab and Gerlach[3] demonstrated the validity of this postulate for a reducing agent in the reaction $Ge + 2MoO_3 \rightarrow GeO_2 + MoO_2$. They showed that Ge doped with n-type dopants (As and Sb) reacted with MoO_3 much faster than Ge doped with p-type dopants (Ga and In). The reactivity of Ge also depended on the concentration of the dopants. Increasing the concentration of the n-type dopants increased the rate of reaction, whereas increasing the concentration of p-type dopants decreased it.

The relationship between the free-energy change of the reaction and the rate (energy of activation) can be explained with the aid of the Ge-MoO$_3$ potential energy diagram in Figure 3. Doping Ge with As increases the number of electrons in the Fermi level (dashed line). Thus n-doped Ge (Ge*) will be at a higher potential than undoped Ge. The activation energy E_a^* for Ge* will be less than the activation energy E_a for undoped Ge, and ΔG^* for Ge* will be less (more negative) than ΔG for undoped Ge. In fact, the change in ΔG due to the doping equals the change in E_a, so that we can divide both by RT to obtain the relation $\Delta G/RT = E_a/RT$, or $\ln K = \alpha \ln k + a$ constant, where K is the equilibrium constant, k is the rate constant, and α is a proportionality constant.

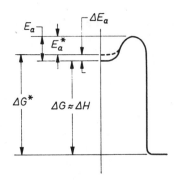

Figure 3. *Potential energy diagram for* Ge-MoO₃ *system³.*

Evans and Polanyi[4], who derived this same equation in a different way, pointed out that the reactions must be very similar for it to apply. No more similar reactions could be imagined than Ge* + MoO₃ vs Ge + MoO₃.

This equation is also quite similar to the linear free-energy relationship of Yoneda[5] and the $\rho\sigma$ law of Hammett.[6] If the Evans-Polanyi equation ever holds quantitatively, it is in just such systems as these.

Altham, McLain and Schwab[2] demonstrated the second half of the semiconductor analogy with the system:

$$NiO + B \rightarrow B_2O_3 + Ni$$

It was shown that NiO doped with Li₂O to increase p-type properties is a much better oxidizer than NiO either undoped or doped with Cr₂O₃.

SOLID-GAS REACTIONS

Catalytic activity of metals and other solids varies with the number and type of imperfections of the catalyst. Anion and cation vacancies, interstitial defects, impurity defects, doping, and Smekal cracks are all important. Stone[1,7] wrote, "Through the application to catalytic problems of the knowledge gained from studies of physics of the solid state, the view that the electronic structure of a solid might be connected with its catalytic activity has become firmly established." Most of this development has occurred fairly recently.

Gray[8] said, "It is already clearly established that any reaction between solids or between a solid and a liquid or gas must be intimately related to the condition of the surface." Two examples, among others that can be cited, illustrate this principle.

In one example, a form of Li_3PO_4 was found to be an excellent catalyst for the rearrangement of propylene oxide to allyl alcohol:

$$\overline{CH_3CHCH_2O} \rightarrow CH_2=CHCH_2OH$$

This could be easily converted to glycerol, $CH_2OH \cdot CHOH\text{-}CH_2OH$, with the addition of Cl and $CA(OH)_2$. However, after this finding, it took several months and many man hours to prepare a second batch of successful catalyst in the laboratory. It was obviously not the chemical nature of Li_3PO_4 but its surface properties, both external and internal, that were so effective.

In the second example, a pyrophoric nickel is used in the preparation of nickel tetracarbonyl:

$$Ni + 4CO \rightarrow NI(CO)_4$$

The Ni is prepared by distilling Hg from an amalgam under vacuum. During carbonyl production, CO is passed over the Ni at room temperature. The reaction proceeds well for a time, but at a certain point the production of carbonyl ceases. It resumes if a very small amount of H_2S is added to the Ni. H_2S is supposedly a catalyst "poison" and this is indeed true if too much is used. These phenomena can be explained by postulating a *gas polishing effect* to account for the cessation of reactivity and a *gas etching effect* to make it resume.

SOLID-LIQUID REACTIONS

Gregg[9] uses the example:

$$CaO + H_2O \rightarrow Ca(OH)_2$$

to show that "in the vast majority of cases where a laboratory or industrial process involves the interaction of a solid with a gas, a liquid, or another solid, the *nature* of the reaction will depend on the *chemical composition* of the solid, but its *rate* will be largely determined by the *mode of pretreatment* of the solid."

DECOMPOSITION REACTIONS

Decomposition reactions are of considerable interest in the chemistry of pyrotechnics. Their applicability is directly related to whether they are endothermic or exothermic.

Endothermic

Some examples of endothermic reactions are:

$$NH_4Cl \rightarrow HCl + NH_3$$
$$CaCO_3 \rightarrow CaO + CO_2$$
$$CuSO_4 \cdot 5H_2O \rightarrow CuSO_4 \cdot 3H_2O \rightarrow CuSO_4 \cdot H_2O \rightarrow CuSO_4$$
$$ZnO + C \rightarrow CO + Zn$$
$$2Fe(OH)_3 \rightarrow Fe_2O_3 + 3H_2O$$
$$Mg(OH)_2 \rightarrow MgO + H_2O$$

Many of these reactions and their analogues have been studied extensively. Their importance to pyrotechnics is primarily as a method of preparing oxidizing agents (see Chapter IV).

Exothermic

Some examples of exothermic reactions are:

$$Pb(N_3)_2 \rightarrow Pb + 3N_2$$
$$NH_4NO_3 \rightarrow N_2O + 2H_2O$$
$$3Pb(OOC)_2 \rightarrow 2PbO + Pb + CO_2 + 2CO$$
$$2KClO_3 \rightarrow 2KCl + 3O_2$$
$$2KClO_4 \rightarrow 2KCl + 4O_2$$

Many exothermic reactions are explosive. Most of these have been treated in depth by Jacobs and Tompkins in Garner[10].

The ignition of ammonium dichromate is one of the more interesting exothermic reactions:

$$(NH_4)_2Cr_2O_7 \rightarrow N_2 + Cr_2O_3 + 4H_2O$$

This reaction was once used fairly widely to provide the *grass* in the fireworks item *Snake in the Grass*. A pyrotechnic *snake* pellet was packaged with loose $(NH_4)_2Cr_2O_7$ in a flattened cylindrical pillbox. Upon ignition of the *snake*-forming mix, the dichromate burned and created the green Cr_2O_3. This reaction is also used for the laboratory simulation of volcanoes described in demonstration manuals.

Similar compounds with internal oxygen balance have been investigated by Shidlovskiy[11]. He reports that $[Co(NH_3)_6][Co(NO_2)_6]$ burns steadily with a heat of combustion of 693 cal/g, and that other complex Co compounds, $Co(NH_3)_2(NO_2)_3$ and $Co(NH_3)_6(NO_2)_3$, had heats of combustion of 667 and 380 cal/g, respectively.

An interesting class of solid-solid reactions was investigated by Henri Moissan about one hundred years ago. An example of this type of reaction studied by the author is the production of Ca_3As_2 by mixing fresh lathe turnings of Ca metal with powdered elemental As and electrically heating the mixture to 450-500 °C in a sealed bomb. After about an hour, the reaction:

$$3Ca + 2As \rightarrow Ca_3As_2$$

was virtually complete, although Ca melts at 842 °C and As sublimes at 613 °C or melts at 817 °C under pressure.

The author had occasion to study this reaction when it became necessary to prepare the arsenide in order to produce arsine and its deuteride from the water reaction:

$$Ca_3As_2 + 6H_2O \rightarrow 2AsH_3 + 3Ca(OH)_2$$

Arsine production was not as straightforward as might be expected because of the heavy and somewhat impervious $Ca(OH)_2$ coating that forms on the unreacted arsenide.

> *Chymists are a strange class of mortals who seem to be compelled to seek their pleasure among smoke and vapor, soot and flame, poisons and poverty, yet among all these evils I seem to live so sweetly that I may die if I would change places with the Persian king.*
>
> J. J. Becher

Chapter III

REFERENCES

1. Stone, F.S., "Lattice Defects in Ionic Crystals," in *Chemistry of the Solid State,* Garner, W.E., Ed., Butterworth, London, 1955 (Available from University Microfilms, Ann Arbor, Mich.).
2. Altham, J.A., McLain, J.H., and Schwab, G.-M., Z. *Physik Chem.* Neue Folge **74,** 121 (1967).
3. Schwab, G.-M. and Gerlach, J., Z. *Physik Chem.* Neue Folge **56,** 121 (1967).
4. Evans, M.G. and Polanyi, M., *Nature* (London) **137,** 530 (1936).
5. Mochida, L. and Honeda, Y., *J. Catal.* **7,** 386 (1967).
6. Hammet, L.P., *Physical Organic Chemistry,* McGraw-Hill, New York, 1940.
7. Stone, F.S., in *Proceedings of the 7th International Symposium on the Reactivity of Solids,* Anderson, J.F., Roberts, M.W., and Stone, F.S., Eds., Chapman and Hall, London, 1972.
8. Gray, T.J., In *Geochemistry of Solids: An Introduction,* Fyfe, W.S., Ed.; McGraw-Hill, New York, 1964.
9. Gregg, S.J., *The Surface Chemistry of Solids,* 2nd ed., Chapman and Hall, London, 1965.
10. Jacobs, P.W.M. and Tompkins, F.C., "Classification and Theory of Solid Reactions," *op. cit.* in reference 1.
11. Shidlovskiy, A.A. et al, *Chem. Abs.* **87,** 70416k (1977).

Chapter IV

REACTIVITY

Für das Reaktionsvermogen fester Stoffe — ist der Beweglichkeitsgrad der massgebliche faktor.

G. F. Hüttig

LATTICE LOOSENESS

Freely translated, the quotation from Hüttig says that some degree of restlessness makes solid state reactions possible. He was referring to the fact that atoms in a crystal are not locked rigidly to the lattice. We use the term "lattice looseness" in the absence of an exact English equivalent to *Beweglichkeitsgrad,* although *looseness* does not convey the same sense of continuous small excursions of the lattice components.

Stone[1] was addressing the same problem of terminology when he lamented the lack of a precise English synonym for the German word that expresses the quality of an almost-perfect crystal structure. He wrote, "The original German term *Fehlordnung* describes the concept of a small departure from complete order more satisfactorily than the English *disorder.*"

In spite of its shortcomings, we will use the word *looseness* (although *rattle* might be more correct) to be consistent with the literature, always keeping in mind that looseness is not a static condition, but that vibrational freedom is very much a part of or antecedent to looseness. As the 17th century English poet, Robert Herrick, wrote about what we might call the *looseness* of his beloved's anatomical *lattice* in a silk dress:

> *Next, when I cast mine eyes and see*
> *That brave vibration, each way free,*
> *O how that glittering taketh me!*

HEDVALL EFFECT AND TAMMANN TEMPERATURE

Hedvall and Tammann were among the early investigators of the relations between lattice vibrations and chemical reactivity. The concepts that bear their names arise from a consideration of the effects of temperature on motion within the lattice.

As the temperature rises, crystal atoms or ions are assumed to vibrate with increasing amplitude about their average positions in the lattice. When this amplitude becomes great enough, the tie to these positions weakens, diffusion is enhanced, and atoms can exchange positions. At relatively low temperatures, this may produce a phase change, a transition from one solid state to another; at higher temperatures (larger vibration amplitudes), the solid may melt.

During such transformations, lattice units are more loosely bound and much more reactive. Enhanced reactivity at or near a transition temperature is called the *Hedvall Effect*. Hauffe[2] states, " . . . the presence of lattice disturbances promotes reactions since place exchange processes are greatly facilitated," and, " . . . solid substances in which there is great disorder and which are often very much loosened by the presence of channels, internal surfaces and other effects of 'microstructure' are generally especially reactive."

A rough measure of lattice loosening is the *Tammann temperature*[3], α, equal to the ratio of the temperature of the solid to its melting point, both temperatures expressed in °K. Thus, ionic surface mobility becomes effective at an α of about 0.3, lattice diffusion (internal mobility) at an α of about 0.5. In NaI (melting point: 651°C, 924°K), for example, surface mobility is significant at about $0.3 \times 924°K = 277°K$, or 4°C, and lattice diffusion at about $0.5 \times 924°K = 462°K$, or 189°C.

Lindemann's equation for the vibrational frequency at the melting point:

$$\nu = \frac{2.8 \, T_m{}^{1/2} \rho^{1/3}}{(\text{Gram formula weight})^{5/6}} \times 10^{12} \text{ Hz}$$

where T_m is the melting point, °K, and ρ is the density in g/cm³, is based on the physical picture of a vibrational amplitude increasing with rising temperature until coulombic forces are no longer strong enough to prevent crystal collapse, or melting. We can use the Lindemann equation to calculate the frequency associated with the Tammann temperature $\alpha = 0.5$ by substituting $T_m/2$ for T_m. The ratio of the frequency at the Tammann temperature *(Tammann frequency)* to that at the melting point *(Lindemann frequency)* is simply $(T_m/2)^{1/2}/T_m{}^{1/2} = (1/2)^{1/2} = 0.707$. That is, the Tammann frequency is 70% of the value required for melting. Another way to regard $\alpha = 0.5$ is that the *Beweglichkeitsgrad* is 70%.

Cancelling the density terms in the Lindemann equation to obtain this frequency ratio is not totally justified since density is obviously less at the melting point than at half that temperature. However, even if a density difference as large at 10% is assumed, the error is only a little over 3% because the frequency varies with the cube root of the density. The approximation is therefore close enough to warrant simplifying the arithmetic.

FACTORS THAT INFLUENCE REACTIVITY

Hedvall[4] has listed the following factors that influence reactivity:

- Deviations from the normal crystallographic or amorphous structure of a substance.
- Lattice defects in the form of hereditary structures.
- Formation of imperfect structures, for example, transitions from one modification to another or on thermal decomposition.
- Presence of guest particles in the lattice.
- Differences in the crystallographic formation of different surfaces.
- Gases which are dissolved in the lattice but which are not themselves chemically reactive in the usual sense.
- Corrosion.
- Adsorption and catalysis.
- Irradiation by absorbable wave lengths.
- Changes in the magnetic state.
- Changes in the electric state.

Selected examples below from the field of pyrotechnics make these generalizations more specific.

Hereditary structures

The reactivity of Fe_2O_3 depends on method of preparation. For example, Hedvall and Sandberg[5] prepared two samples, one by igniting $Fe_2(SO_4)_3$ and the other by igniting $Fe_2(C_2O_4)_3$, and then studied their reaction with CaO at increasing temperatures. The results, plotted in Figure 1, showed that, at 750 °C, three times as much CaO reacted with Fe_2O_3 derived from the sulfate than with Fe_2O_3 derived from the oxalate.

The sulfate-derived oxide was more reactive despite the fact that its average particle size was larger than that of the oxalate product, which would normally be expected to inhibit reactivity. However, x-ray powder diffraction patterns of Fe_2O_3 prepared by the ignition of the sulfate at temperatures below 650 °C revealed a relatively loose crystal structure, i.e., less sharply defined crystallinity, compared with the patterns obtained with the oxalate-derived

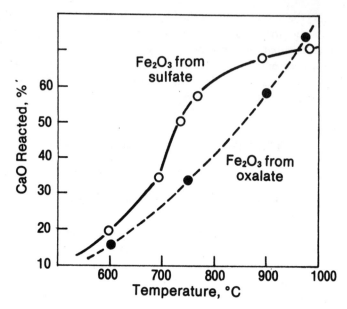

Figure 1. *Dependence of* Fe_2O_3 *reactivity on method of preparation*[5].

Fe_2O_3. In this case, the looser internal structure "inherited" from the method of preparation was more influential than particle size.

Figure 1 contains another point of interest. The two curves intersect above 900 °C, after which the more active oxide is the one derived from the oxalate. Evidently, at the higher temperatures, the combination of smaller particle size (greater surface area) and increased mobility of lattice constituents overcomes the initial disadvantage of a tighter crystal structure. This conjecture was confirmed by heating the sulfate-derived Fe_2O_3 to 900 °C for 30 minutes and then retesting its x-ray diffraction pattern and reactivity. The pattern did become more sharply defined after the annealing process and the reactivity over the full temperature range did become the same as that of the oxalate-derived oxide.

Although the term annealing is more commonly used by metallurgists to describe the heat treatment for relief of strains in metallic lattices, it is also applicable to the relief of ionic lattice strains. This is apparent in later experiments by Pryor and Evans[6] on the relation between ignition temperature and solubility in HCl which tended to confirm the findings of Hedvall and Sandberg that Fe_2O_3 has a denser lattice and is less reactive when prepared at 900 °C than at lower temperatures. Their data are shown in Figure 2. The curve indicates that higher ignition temperatures are associated with lower solubility. The underlying principle is that higher temperatures give sufficient kinetic

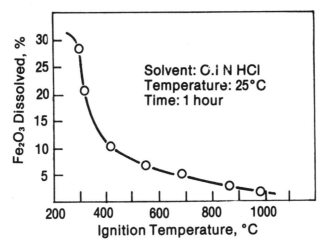

Figure 2. *Correlation between solubility and ignition temperature of* Fe_2O_3[6].

energy to constituents in a distorted lattice to enable them to migrate to steady state lattice positions.

Two personal experiences also illustrate the great variation in reactivity of Fe_2O_3. A first-fire composition used to ignite a thermite-filled munition contained 70% Fe_2O_3 and 30% Ti. When prepared with CP reagent grade Fe_2O_3, the mix would not ignite at all from primer flash and only with difficulty from a bunsen-burner flame. However, when the same Ti powder was mixed with pigment-grade Fe_2O_3, ignition was easy and burning uniform.

Fe_2O_3 is also used in a device called the *Pyronol Torch* (see Chapter VIII). The mixture is a modified thermite of Fe_2O_3, Ni, Al, and $(C_2F_2)n$, and can cut through 4 inches of steel in about 0.25 sec. However, depending upon the Fe_2O_3 type used, penetration time can vary from 0.15 to 0.50 sec.

Crystal form

Crystal form strongly affects the impact sensitivity of the explosive HMX, as shown in the following table from McCrone[7]:

Table I. Impact sensitivity of HMX vs crystal form

System	Orthorhombic	Monoclinic	Monoclinic	Hexagonal
Habit (shape)	Rods & needles	Needles	Plates	Rods
Sensitivity (drop weight)	2-30	1-33	1-20	1-10

$KClO_3$ is another example of a substance for which crystal form affects reactivity. Buckley[8] crystallized $KClO_3$ from several dye solutions, obtaining different crystal forms, and found that reactivity varied widely. More specifically, Kaslin[9] found that $KClO_3$ reactivity in match-head formulations varied, in descending order, as the crystal form varied from needles to thin lamellae to near-spherical nodules. McLain and Lewis[10], in differential thermal analyses of the $S-KClO_3$ reaction, obtained different reactivities with $KClO_3$ crystallized from solutions of methyl orange, Congo red, or the household detergents Dreft or Tide.

Irradiation

As might be expected, radiation of high enough energy can dislodge atoms from their normal lattice positions to create vacancies and interstitial atoms. In many semiconductors, where imperfections are the source of moderate electrical conduction, irradiation increases conductivity because it increases the abundance of imperfections. In metals, however, where normal properties depend on crystal orderliness, the disorder caused by irradiation decreases the normally high conductivity, and also decreases ductility and malleability. As with semiconductors, irradiation increases the chemical reactivity of metals. Of special interest to the chemist is the energy stored in lattice defects, which may amount to hundreds of calories per mol, and makes the crystal more reactive, more easily decomposed, and a more potent catalyst, oxidizer, or reducer.

In azide studies, Papazian[11] has modified the infrared absorption spectrum of NaN_3 crystals by irradiating them, and Bryant[12] has given convincing evidence that irradiated alkali metal azides contain excited azide ions. Radiation effects on azides also have practical consequences. For example, exposure of dextrinated lead azide to strong ultraviolet rays not only turns its color from cream to cafe au lait, but also increases its impact and friction sensitivity to the point where it is almost impossible to compact the powder in loading primer detonators without frequent explosions in the presses.

Mechanically enhanced reactivity

Although not explicitly included in Hedvall's list of factors that affect reactivity, mechanical working can bring several of the listed factors into play simultaneously. For example, consider the solid-solid reaction:

$$3CuO + 2Al \rightarrow Al_2O_3 + 3Cu + heat$$

If the heats of formation, ΔH_f, of the elements in their standard state is zero, then the release of heat, ΔH, in the reaction is:

$$\Delta H = \Delta H_f(Al_2O_3) - 3 \Delta H_f(CuO) = 287.7 \text{ kcal}$$

However, this is true only if the energy required to break the Al-Al bonds exactly equals that recovered by formation of Cu-Cu bonds. If some is not so recovered, the heat of reaction will be reduced. In practice, this reaction creates so high a temperature that some Cu-Cu bond energy is lost because the copper evolves as a monatomic gas. (This composition is an excellent propellant! It can send a 45-cm length of 3/4-inch pipe soaring to a height of 400 ft.)

One way to get all the heat out of the reaction would be to start with atomic Al. So far, nobody has devised a grinder to accomplish this feat, but we try to approach it by milling, pulverizing, atomizing, and grinding the metal to break as many Al-Al bonds as possible before use. When we break an Al macrocrystal into pieces, we also create new surfaces, edges, and corners at which atoms are not bonded as strongly as internal atoms. Instead of a coordination number of 12, some of these atoms have as few as three or four nearest neighbors and require considerably less energy to pull apart. Two other major advantages of fine particle size are increased homogeneity in the mix and more contact between reactants, which facilitate diffusion.

Grinding is not the only way to create more surface or to break or weaken Al-Al bonds. Anything that loosens the lattice also accomplishes this result, whether it be Smekal cracks, vacancies, or internal surface. Dopants such as Si and Li, properly used[13], can weaken Al-Al bonds before grinding.

The mere dividing of crystals into smaller pieces (neglecting other effects of pulverization) does not contribute significantly to bond breaking or crystal loosening, as measured by the exposure of relatively larger numbers of atoms at particle surfaces. We can easily calculate this effect.

For example, Al has a gram molecular weight of 27 g and a density of 2.7 g/cm³, so one mol, which contains 6.02×10^{23} atoms, occupies a volume of 10 cm³. For convenience, let us assume that an Al powder passes through a 200-mesh screen and that a typical particle is a cube about 1.4×10^{-2} cm (140 μ) on a side. The particle volume is therefore 2.74×10^{-6} cm³ and holds 1.65×10^{17} atoms. The particle's six faces have a total area of 1.18×10^{-3} cm². If we also assume that the surface layer of atoms is 5×10^{-8} cm (5 Å) thick, then the total volume of the six surface layers is 5.90×10^{-11} cm³, and the number of surface atoms is 3.55×10^{12}.

The ratio of more vulnerable surface atoms to the total number is therefore $(3.55 \times 10^{12})/(1.65 \times 10^{17}) = 2.15 \times 10^{-5}$, or 0.00215%. Thus, in a 140-μ particle, 99.998% of the atoms are inner ones. Even in a particle one-tenth this size, internal atoms still constitute 99.98% of the total. Such increases are too slight to be detected with a calorimeter. Then how can we account for the effect of particle size on the reaction of a 50:50 red lead-ferrosilicon mix, published by Nakahara[14] and shown in Table II?

Table II. Effect of particle size on reaction

Fe-Si Mean Particle Size, μ	22	16	14	9.3	8.0	6.2
Heat of Reaction, cal/g	176.7	182.5	185.2	189.3	192.2	196.8

Naeser and Scholz[15] provide a plausible explanation. These investigators passed powders through a rolling mill just before testing. Some of their findings are:

Rolled dolomite sintered at a temperature 100-150 °C lower than did unrolled dolomite of the same particle size.

The reaction temperature of:

$$Fe_2O_3 + SiO_2 \rightarrow Fe_2SiO_5$$

is as much as 200 °C lower for rolled than for unrolled reactants.

Rolled Cr_2O_3 placed in a stream of H_2 at 1250 °C reduced to Cr while unrolled material remained a green powder under the same conditions.

Rolled Fe_2O_3 reduced at a temperature 80 °C lower than did unrolled powder. However, annealing the rolled Fe_2O_3 for one hour at 900 °C before the test eliminated the difference.

NiO, Mo_2O_3, and W_2O_3 behaved in a similar fashion.

From experiments with CuO, they calculated the amount of energy added by the mechanical rolling process. Since rolled CuO reacts with 10% HCl at 200 °C, while unrolled powder required 240 °C, they reasoned that the energy added by rolling should equal the heat required to raise the CuO temperature from 200 °C to 240 °C. The specific heat of CuO (0.0115 kcal/mol °C) multiplied by the temperature rise (40 °C) = 0.460 kcal/mol, or 5.78 cal/g (CuO gram formula weight is 79.54).

To test this supposition, they performed five trials each with rolled and unrolled CuO, dissolving precise 2.000-g samples in 10% HCl and measuring the heat of solution calorimetrically. The results were:

Unrolled CuO   121.2 ± 0.6 cal/g
Rolled CuO   125.8 ± 0.7 cal/g

The difference of 4.6 ± 1.3 cal/g compares favorably with the calculated value of 5.78 cal/g.

These results tend to support the hypothesis that milling enhances reactivity not so much by particle size reduction as by lattice deformation, although the two may be unavoidably linked.

Another example of this phenomenon appears in the work by Clark and Rowan[16] on yellow and red PbO. They converted the yellow oxide into the red by three hours of ball milling. (Red PbO reacts with and absorbs O_2 much faster than yellow PbO does, and is also a better catalyst for the decomposition of H_2O_2). The red PbO showed lattice faults in x-ray diffraction patterns, which vanished after 3.5 hours of annealing at 400 °C and 500 °C.

Other examples are two double salts: Ag_2HgI_4, which is yellow at room temperature, turns red at 42 °C, and reverts to yellow on cooling; and Cu_2HgI_4, which is red at room temperature, turns violet at 70 °C, and reverts to red on cooling. Milling causes these double salts to change color instantly and permanently without requiring a temperature rise. The usual colors can be restored by heating the salts to 100-150 °C for some time and allowing them to cool slowly.

Gregg's work on kaolin[17] deserves specific mention. Prolonged dry grinding of solids usually reaches a *grinding equilibrium* when the rate of production of new surface by disintegration equals the rate of loss of surface by aggregation. Gregg found that this did not occur with kaolin. After 500 hours of milling, the specific surface attained a maximum of 54 m²/g. At 600 hours, however, it had fallen to 42m²/g and continued to fall until it reached 38 m²/g at 1000 hours. Notwithstanding the decrease in specific surface, the kaolin became much more reactive, as tested by solution in 0.75N HCl. After 1000 hours of grinding, 58% dissolved in 48 hours at room temperature, whereas the solubility of unground kaolin was negligible. Although part of the increased solubility was due to an increase in surface area, the fact that the amount dissolved *per unit area* increased steadily from 0.65%/m² at 500 hours to 1.25%/m² at 1000 hours made it clear that grinding had enhanced kaolin's activity. X-ray diffraction patterns supplied corroborating evidence as they became increasingly blurred with longer grinding.

In another instance, McLain and Lewis[10] found by differential thermal analysis that freshly ground and mixed S-$KClO_3$ mixtures had lower ignition temperatures and sharper pre-ignition reaction slopes than usual.

Adsorption

Adsorption can be either activating or inhibiting. Consider first an example of adsorptive inhibition.

Severe difficulties were encountered in procuring a standardized ZnO for use in the HC Type C smoke mix (Al, ZnO, C_2Cl_6). It was believed that the major variations in performance (quantity of smoke, color, and burning rate) were due to differences in particle size. In an attempt to obtain uniform particle size and burning characteristics, Lydy and McLain[18] studied the effects of calcination on seven samples of ZnO selected for their widely different

burning rates in the HC smoke mix. Samples were calcined in a rotary tubular
furnace at 900-1000 °C for 30-45 minutes. As expected, the average particle
size (determined by electron microscopy) increased for all samples. However,
burning rates also increased. Chemical analysis explained this apparent anomaly
by showing that the heat treatment reduced the quantities of CO_2 (or $ZnCO_3$),
moisture (from $Zn(OH)_2$), water soluble salt, and sulfur in the material. In
addition, heating had virtually eliminated the tendency to readsorb moisture
and CO_2. Although the burning rates of mixes containing calcined ZnO
were quite fast, they were also quite uniform and could be easily and repro-
ducibly slowed by the addition of 1-2% of zinc borate.

Black powder presents an example of adsorptive activation. It has been
standard manufacturing practice for many years to mill the S and charcoal
together before mixing with KNO_3. Chemists know by the nose test that
flowers of S oxidize in air to SO_2. They are also familiar with the enormous
adsorptive capacity of charcoal, indicated in Table III by data from Gregg[19]:

Table III. Charcoal adsorptivity

Adsorbed Gas	Adsorption cm³/g @ 25 °C, 760 mm Hg
NH_3	136
SO_2	97.5
N_2O	67.0
C_2H_2	64.7
CO_2	60.1
C_2H_4	54.7
CO	14.1
N_2	10.9
H_2	1.8

The reactive properties of charcoal depend heavily on its adsorption heritage.
Gregg's list shows that SO_2 will displace all gases except NH_3 from charcoal.
Thus, the SO_2 from the S in the black powder mix is adsorbed preferentially
by the charcoal and increases the charcoal's reactivity to oxidation.

Guest particles - doping

Supersensitive $KClO_3$. $KClO_3$ has been made supersensitive by dissolving
it in distilled water and adding 2.8 mole % (based on dry weight) of $Cu(ClO_3)_2$
$\cdot 6H_2O$. Water was distilled off under oil-pump vacuum at 65-70 °C (the copper salt decomposes at 100 °C). The residual pale blue laminar crystals were
dried in an oven for 24 hours at 68 ± °C.

1.23 g of the dried, doped chlorate was then mixed with 0.48 g of purified S and ground gently in an agate mortar with an agate pestle behind a barricade. The pulverized mixture was placed in a 10-ml plastic-capped glass vial and allowed to stand behind a barricade. After 30 minutes, a spontaneous, high-order (very loud) detonation occurred which destroyed the vial and cap without trace and left a small crater and burn marks on the table top. The procedure and result were reproducible.

Highly reactive Fe_2O_3. Doping by means of cocrystallization has made Fe_2O_3 especially reactive. During work on the *Pyronol Torch*, (see chapter VIII), large regular crystals of $CuSO_4 \cdot FeSO_4 \cdot xH_2O$ and $NiSO_4 \cdot FeSO_4 \cdot xH_2O$ were grown from an acidic solution of the two salts and then decomposed in a current of O_2 at 200-250 °C. This not only improved the cutting ability of the torch, but also increased the calorific value of a 50:50 Fe_2O_3-Ti mixture. Cocrystals of $FeSO_4$ and sulfates of Mn, Mg, and Zn were also prepared in this manner.

The same methods can also be used to prepare very efficient ferrites for magnetic memory devices in computers.[20]

Reactive NiO. Work on NiO cited in Chapter III (references 2 and 5) can usefully be discussed further here because it illustrates the extent to which doping can alter the reactivity of a nonstoichiometric material. The results of doping NiO with Li_2O and Cr_2O_3, determined by differential thermal analysis, are shown in Figure 3 and in Table IV.

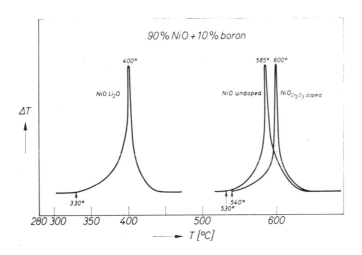

Figure 3. *Differential thermal analysis of mix containing B and doped NiO (Ch. III, ref. 2).*

The extent of the enhanced reactivity can be dramatized by application to the smelting process for Ni. The data show that a form of NiO can be made which will reduce to Ni at a temperature 200 °C below that of ordinary NiO! The savings in heat in the smelting process would be enormous. This work also shows that the nature of the impurity is extremely important and selective doping can yield a range of reactivities.

Table IV. Differential thermal analysis of doped NiO.

System	Start of Exotherm $\pm 5\,°C$	Peak of Exotherm $\pm 5\,°C$
$B + NiO_{Li_2O}$	330	400
$B + NiO_{undoped}$	530	585
$B + NiO_{Cr_2O_3}$	540	600
$Ge + NiO_{Li_2O}$	350	418
$Ge + NiO_{Cr_2O_3}$	535	575
$Si + NiO_{Li_2O}$	715	725
$Si + NiO_{Cr_2O_3}$	no reaction through 1040	

Hedvall and Tammann effects

Spice and Staveley[21] studied reaction rates in some twenty solid systems and concluded that "the rate of burning was more sensitive to the chemical nature of the oxidizing agent than to that of the metal." Their findings can be explained by realizing that, in most cases, the oxidizer has the lower melting point (Tammann), transition temperature (Hedvall), or decomposition temperature. Thus, it is the oxidizer that is of paramount importance in at least the incipient phase of a reaction.

Only a small number of oxidizers are important to the pyrotechnic industry. They are listed in Table V with pertinent data from Ellern[22].

The versatile delay mix D16, which contains $PbCrO_4$, $BaCrO_4$, and Mn, is a useful example because it permits us to compare the reaction of a given reductant with two compounds that have the same oxidizing anion coupled to different cations. D16's burning rate can be varied by changing the proportions in the composition as shown by data in Table VI also from Ellern. The data clearly indicate that increasing the amount of $BaCrO_4$ at the expense of $PbCrO_4$ markedly slows down the reaction. Why is $PbCrO_4$ a faster oxidizer than $BaCrO_4$? It is because $PbCrO_4$ has a much lower melting point than $BaCrO_4$, and also undergoes a transition at 707 °C whereas $BaCrO_4$ has no transition.

Table V. Oxidizers used in pyrotechnics
(Alphabetically by anion)

Anions	Cation	Formula	Melting Point °C	Decomposition Temperature °C	Transition Temperature °C
Chlorates	Barium	$Ba(ClO_3)_2 \cdot H_2O$	-	120	-
		$Ba(ClO_3)_2$	414	-	-
	Lithium	$LiClO_3$	127.6	-	-
	Potassium	$KClO_3$	368.4	400	-
	Sodium	$NaClO_3$	248-260	-	-
Chromates	Barium	$BaCrO_4$	*	*	*
	Calcium	$CaCr_4 \cdot 2H_2O$	-	200	-
		$CaCrO_4$	-	750	-
	Lead	$PbCrO_4$	844	600	707
	Potassium	K_2CrO_4	968.3	-	-
Dichromates	Ammonium	$(NH_4)_2Cr_2O_7$	-	170	-
	Potassium	$K_2Cr_2O_7$	-	500	398
Iodates	Lead	$Pb(IO_3)_2$	-	300	-
	Potassium	KIO_3	560	-	-
	Silver	$AgIO_3$	>200	Decomposes	-
					IV→III 32.1
Nitrates	Amonium	NH_4NO_3	169.6	210	III→II 84.2
					II→I 125.2
	Barium	$Ba(NO_3)_2$	592	>600	-
	Guanidinium	$NH_2 \cdot C(NH)NH_3NO_3$	214	-	-
	Potassium	KNO_3	334	400	127.8
	Silver	$AgNO_3$	212	-	160
	Sodium	$NaNO_3$	306.8	380	155
	Strontium	$Sr(NO_3)_2$	570	-	-
Nitroguanidine		$NH_2 \cdot C(NH)NHNO_2$	246	-	-
Oxides	Barium	BaO_2	450	800	-
	Copper	Cu_2O	1235	1800	-
		CuO	-	1026	-
	Iron	Fe_2O_3	1565	-	-
		Fe_3O_4	-	1538	-
	Lead	PbO_2	-	290	-
		Pb_3O_4	-	500	-
		PbO	888	-	-
	Manganese	MnO_2	-	535	-
	Molybdenum	MoO_3	795	Sublimes	-
	Strontium		-	860	-
	Tungsten	WO_3	1473	-	-
	Zinc	ZnO	>1800	Sublimes	-
Perchlorates	Ammonium	NH_4ClO_4	Decomposes	-	-
	Barium	$Ba(ClO_4)_2$	505	-	-
	Calcium	$Ca(ClO_4)_2$	-	-	-
	Potassium	$KClO_4$	600	510-610	-
	Sodium	$NaClO_4$	-	482	-
Permanganates	Potassium	$KMnO_4$	-	>240	-
Sufates	Barium	$BaSO_4$	1580	-	-
	Calcium	$CaSO_4$	1450	-	1193
Sulfur	-	S	99.5	-	112.8, 132

*Data unavailable. Heat of formation is 1398 kJ/mol for $BaCrO_4$ and 913 kJ/mol for $PbCrO_4$, indicating that $BaCrO_4$ is the more stable compound.

Table VI. Burning time vs composition

Mn, %	44	39	37	33
BaCrO₄, %	3	14	20	31
PbCrO₄, %	53	47	43	36
Burning time, sec/in	3.7	5.8	8.7	13.5

Several other systems with pairs of oxidizers also illustrate this point, including W, Ni/Zr, and Mo delays for which the oxidizers are $KClO_4$ and $BaCrO_4$. The Mo delays are the most striking, and the data in Table VII, also from Ellern, display very well the tendency toward shorter burning times as the less stable $KClO_4$ portion is increased and/or the more stable $BaCrO_4$ portion is decreased.

Table VII. Molybdenum delay burning time vs composition

Mo, %	80-89	80	55	35	30
BaCrO₄, %	0	10	40	55	65
KClO₄, %	20-11	10	5	10	5
Burning time, sec/in	0.01-0.04	0.1	2	6	18

The above discussion can be used to illustrate three kinds of knowledge that may be applied to pyrotechnic problems. For example, suppose that a batch of D16 delay mix has been made but its burning rate is too low for the batch to be put on the loading line. An experienced pyrotechnician would increase the rate by adding $PbCrO_4$, Mn, or both, i.e., the faster oxidizer and the better heat conductor. If asked why he chose one particular remedy, he would probably answer that he had tried it before and it worked, or someone had told him previously how to speed up the mix. These are knowledge of the first and second kinds: empirical experience and specific instruction. Knowledge of the third kind is basic understanding, i.e., theory. It has greater value because it enables one to correct a problem even in relatively new systems with which one has had little experience and for which guidelines are not yet established.

Fluxes

A.J.E. Welch in his chapter in Garner[23] writes, "Deliberate addition of 'impurities' to accelerate solid-solid reactions is frequent in practical applications, but most of the additives (often loosely termed 'fluxes') are materials which reduce the lowest eutectic temperature effective in the mixture, and thus introduce a small amount of liquid phase."

Dr. H. C. Clauser used to say that "water was the cheapest and best catalyst of them all" for fireworks compositions, and that the role of water vapor in accelerating pyrotechnic reactions is well recognized if not well understood. For example, the burning rate and color quality of fireworks star compositions depend markedly upon very small changes in the moisture content as shown in Figure 4[24].

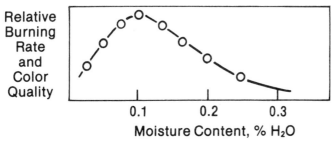

Figure 4. *Effect of moisture on fireworks star performance.*

A similar phenomenon has been observed in PbO_2-Si electric blasting-cap delays[25]. Static hazards require mixing and loading the delays into hermetically sealed units in a humidified atmosphere. Tests after three days' storage indicated that burning rates had increased by up to 25%. McLain and McClure[26] studied extensively the effect of moisture content on the colored-smoke fuel mix $KClO_3$-$NaHCO_3$-S. Differential thermal analyses of mixes stored in desiccators at various relative humidities are summarized in Table VIII. They show that the intake of small amounts of moisture (values proved to be about 0.3-0.5%) tends to accelerate the reaction (lower the ignition temperature). Higher moisture content (longer storage and/or higher desiccator humidity) tends to have little effect or may even retard the reaction. (Also see General Reference 21 on moisture effects.)

Table VIII. Ignition temperature of colored smoke mix vs storage humidity
(Temperatures in °C)

Storage Time, hr	Relative Humidity, %						
	0	3.2	8.5	47.2	88.8	97.5	100
0	164	164	164	164	164	164	164
24	152	157	142	147	147	172	177
48	147	137	152	137	157	172	172
72	172	147	172	157	152	182	177
120	152	147	142	162	162	167	197
360	177	147	172	162	157	192	182
744	162	152	172	177	177	−	−

Phlegmatizing agents (inhibitors)

Ubbelohde[27] wrote, "Incorporation of phlegmatizing substances in the solid can greatly modify the course of a thermal decomposition leading to a detonation. Thus lead azide can be caused to crystallize with the incorporation of starch or dextrin separating microcrystals in a polycrystalline granule. These layers of dextrin altogether modify the activation energy controlling thermal decomposition leading up to detonation."

Dextrin-coated lead azide was used throughout World War II to reduce mixing, loading, and handling hazards. Two other phlegmatizing agents have since replaced it. These are a sodium carboxymethyl cellulose, used in the Explosives Research and Development Establishment's RD 1333[28], and a polyvinyl alcohol-coated azide[29] which not only reduce the hazards but also allow more sensitivity to flame actuation and greater output from smaller charges. Today, the RD 1333 azide is the most widely used.

Protection against corrosion

Chemical treatment to protect against corrosion is also a form of inhibition. Bonderizing, Irridite, and Chronak, to name just a few anticorrosion processes, have been used for many years to lengthen the life of the more reactive metals. Passivation by acid dip is also noteworthy in decreasing surface attack, as is the oxide layer that forms on Al and Zn. Virtually all these methods rely on the formation of an inert coating tightly bonded to the metal surface.

SUMMARY

It can be seen from the foregoing that almost everything one does to a solid enhances reactivity. This is so because disturbance is more likely to loosen than tighten the lattice and to increase rather than decrease the degree of *rattle*. The effect is predominantly structural as evidenced by the NiO studies. Even though doping NiO with Cr_2O_3 reduces its conductivity and thereby its reactivity, the accompanying physical disturbance almost counterbalances the chemical effect so that the decrease in reactivity is very small. The same effect has been noted with metals. In theory, it should be possible to dope a metal to make it much less reactive, but this has never been accomplished. Successful methods of decreasing reactivity have involved surface barriers such as a coating that covers flaws or an adsorbed layer of an inhibiting gas. An exception is heat treatment or annealing, as in the case of Fe_2O_3, which energizes displaced ions in the lattice and enables them to find positions of greater stability.

Imbricate layers in serried stacks
With flaws, dislocations, jogs and cracks.

Chapter IV
REFERENCES

1. Stone, F.S., "Lattice Defects in Ionic Crystals," in *Chemistry of the Solid State,* Garner, W.E., Ed., Butterworth, London, 1955 (Available from University Microfilms, Ann Arbor, Mich.).

2. Hauffe, K., *Reaktionen in und an festen stoffen,* Springer Verlag, Berlin, 1955; Vols. I and II.

3. Tammann, G., *Zeit. f. anorg. Chem.* **149,** 21-98 (1925).

4. Hedvall, J.A., *Solid State Chemistry, Whence, Where and Whither,* Elsevier. London, 1966.

5. Hedvall, J.A. and Sandberg, S.O., *Z. anorg. u. allge. Chem.* **24,** 15 (1938).

6. Pryor, M.J. and Evans, U.R., *J. Chem. Soc.* London, 1949, p. 181.

7. McCrone, W.C., *Ordnance,* 1959, p. 506.

8. Buckley, H.E., *Mem. Proc. Manchester Lit. and Phil. Soc.* **92,** 77-123, (1950-51).

9. Kaslin, R., *Chemie und Industrie* **57,** 444 (1947).

10. McLain, J.H. and Lewis, D.V., *Effect of Phase Change in Solid-Solid Reactions,* Report WCDC 6465, Grant DA-AMC-18-035-77(A), Chemical Research and Development Laboratories, Edgewood Arsenal, Md., 1965.

11. Papazian, H.A., *J. Phys. Chem. Solids* **21,** 81 (1961) and **27,** 906 (1966).

12. Bryant, J.I., *J. Chem. Phys.* **42,** 2270 (1965).

13. Hall, R.L. and Ratliff, O.D., *An Al-Si alloy for use in propellants to increase specific impulse,* U.S. Patent 3,053,708 (1962).

14. Nakahara, S., *J. Ind. Explos. Soc.* (Japan) **21,** 363-374 (1960).

15. Naeser, G. and Scholz, W., *Kolloid Zeitschrift* **156,** 1-8 (1958).

16. Clark, G.L. and Rowan, R., *J. Am. Chem. Soc.* **61,** 58 (1939) and **63,** 1302 (1941).

17. Gregg, S.J., *The Surface Chemistry of Solids,* 2nd ed., Chapman and Hall, London, 1965, pp.303 ff.

18. Lydy, C.M. and McLain, J.H., *Calcination of Zinc Oxides for HC Smoke,* TDMR 1137, Edgewood Arsenal, Md., 1945.

19. Gregg, S.J., *op. cit.,* p. 33.

20. McLain, J.H., *Process for Preparation of Ferrites,* U.S. Patent 3,837,479 (1975).

21. Spice, J.E. and Staveley, L.A.K., *J. Soc. Chem. Ind.* **68,** 313-319 (1949).

22. Ellern, H., *Military and Civilian Pyrotechnics,* Chemical Publishing Co., New York, 1968.

23. Welch, A.J.E., in *Chemistry of the Solid State,* Garner, W.E., Ed., Butterworth, London, 1955 (available from University Microfilms, Ann Arbor, Mich.).

24. Private communication from Moog and Nicolaus Fireworks, Wuppertal, West Germany.

25. Private communication from Wetterholm, Nitro-Nobel, Gyttorp, Sweden.

26. McLain, J.H. and McClure, M.D., *Effects of Phase Change in Solid-Solid Reactions, Final Report,* Grant DA-AMC-18-035-77(A), Chemical Research and Development Laboratories, Edgewood Arsenal, Md., April 1968.

27. Ubbelohde, A.R., *op. cit.* in reference 23; Chapter 11.

28. Taylor, G.W.C. and Napier, S.E., British Patent 828,148 (1960).

29. Fleischer, J. and Burtle, J.C., U.S. Patent 2,421,778 (1947).

Chapter V

DELAYS

By delay he restored the state.
Quintus Ennius 239-169 B.C.

Pyrotechnic delays are obviously not what Quintus Ennius had in mind, but serve a useful purpose in their own way for allowing a desired interval (burning time) between an impulse and a later action. They have wide ranging application in industry and ordnance as ignition sources as well as delays. They are vital to delay blasting caps, fuses, and initiators of all types such as squibs, detonators, and primers. Those delay mixes that involve solids reacting with solids to form solids have the important property of "gaslessness" which enhances the reproducibility of burning rate in sealed assemblies. (Gaslessness is like purity; it is approached, but never totally achieved.)

HISTORY

The first pyrotechnic delays probably were the fireworks fuses which Chinese artisans in the 6th and 7th centuries made in the form of tissue-paper wrapped cores of black powder. An Englishman, William Bickford of Cornwall, also used wrapped black powder in the early 1800s to produce a *safety fuse* in thread-and-lead covers[1]. Throughout World War I and during the early years of World War II, the same sheathed black-powder cores were still the only standardized delay trains.

However, in 1943 O.G. Bennett[2] developed a Ni-$KClO_4$-superfloss delay which was standardized by the U.S. Army and used in the M204, M205, and

M206 hand-grenade fuses. This was the first of the so-called *gasless* delay mixes, although G.C. Hale[3] of Picatinny Arsenal had also done much work in this field in attempts to achieve gaslessness for use in antiaircraft rounds. It was hoped that gasless delays would minimize the extreme effect of ambient pressure on the burning times of black-powder mixes then available. The Bennett delay has since been replaced by a mix using a Ni-Zr alloy developed by D. Hart.[4]

Early in 1944, another gasless delay train was developed by McLain and Ruble[5] at Edgewood Arsenal for the M201 hand-grenade fuse. This mix was bipartite in that it had a first-fire or ignition mix comprised of Pb_3O_4, Mn, and Si, and a delay mix containing PbO, Si, and fuller's earth. These mixes lent themselves to binding with a small percentage of celluloid-acetone solution, granulation while in a moist state, and graphiting after the granules were dried. The mixes could then be pelleted in an automatic pelleting press and conveniently loaded by reconsolidation into any size container.

The motivation for development of the Bennett and M201 mixes was not only to manage the ambient pressure problem but also to achieve two other desirable features: solid slag-forming reaction products that produce a gas seal, and nonhygroscopic ingredients that survive high humidity storage and use. The number of gasless delay mixes has since increased dramatically to include virtually every type of delay and ignition-mix application.

The work described above was accomplished during wartime. Theory was ignored under the exigencies to achieve as quickly as possible a safe, reproducible, high-performance, storable delay train which could be manufactured with high efficiency. Lamentably, in the more than thirty years following the close of hostilities, although many new and effective mixes have been developed and used, relatively little effort has gone into advancing the theory of the solid-solid self-propagating reaction on which delays are based.

THEORY

Spice and Staveley

Although theory was largely neglected, there were significant contributions. Previous mention of the excellent and important work of Spice and Staveley[6] included only the portions proving that the preignition reaction was a true solid-solid process. The following is a more complete summary of their findings:

Delivered heats of reaction were never as high as calculated.
Reactions delivered maximum heat for compositions containing more than the expected percentage of the least abundant component.

A composition that gave the maximum burning rate usually gave the maximum heat of reaction.

Burning rate and sensitivity to ignition spark depended mainly on the nature of the oxidant.

Stoichiometry could be ascertained by plotting Q (the heat emitted by that quantity of mix containing one gram formula weight of oxidizer) versus the percent reductant.

Hill et al

The next papers of importance to the theory of delays were by Hill and coworkers[7,8]. By developing a special thermocouple technique for measuring the pertinent variables, the Hill group was more successful than Spice and Staveley had been in finding agreement between delay performance and the Maillard and LeChatelier equation:

$$v = \frac{kq}{bc^2 \rho \, (T_i - T_o)}$$

where v = burning rate in cm/sec
k = thermal conductivity in cal/cm sec °C
q = heat of reaction in cal/gm
b = reaction zone width in cm
c = specific heat in cal/g°C
ρ = density in g/cm^3
T_i = burning temperature in °C
T_o = ambient temperature in °C

Their contribution can be summarized as follows:

Excellent agreement with the Maillard and Le Chatelier equation in truly solid-solid systems, especially if they contained a high percentage of a good heat conductor.

A method for measuring activation energies that was superior to that of Henkin and McGill[9].

A combined mathematical and experimental approach that yielded a clearer physical model than was previously available.

Nakahara [10], Boys and Corner[11], and Booth[12] were also active in this area.

It should be mentioned that the empirical propagation index of McLain[13], used successfully to design and develop delay trains during World War II, has been modified and expanded by Rose[14]. To the original index:

$$P_I = \frac{\Delta H}{T_i}$$

where ΔH is the heat of reaction and T_i the burning temperature, Rose added the density, ρ, and the burning rate, BR, to obtain:

$$P_I = \frac{(\Delta H)\,\rho\,(BR)}{T_i}$$

and recommended that "Government and private industrial manufacturers of pyrotechnic compositions used in ordnance should consider both indices as comparative screening criteria for pyrotechnic compositions." Burning rate theory has also been studied by Johnson[15] and McLain[16] using the basic heat transfer equation.

Classical kinetic theory

Classical physical chemical theory is based on two postulates:

Molecules must collide to react.
Collision is necessary but not sufficient; colliding molecules must also have enough energy (E_a) to react.

and is expressed by the Arrhenius equation:

$$k = se^{-E_a/RT}$$

where: k is the reaction rate constant
     s is the space factor
    E_a is the activation energy
    R is the gas constant
    T is the absolute temperature

Since E_a is the numerator of a negative exponent, the reaction rate increases as E_a decreases.

Activation energies can be determined empirically from the logarithmic form of the Arrhenius equation:

$$\log k = -E_a/2.303RT + \log s$$

by plotting $\log k$ versus $1/T$ and measuring the slope of the resulting straight line. Very few reactions have been found with E_a greater than 100,000 cal. Those with E_a smaller than 5000 cal are extremely fast. Table I lists E_a values measured by Hill et al[7] for several systems. In practice, the mixtures had surprisingly slow burning rates for such low activation energies, probably because the measured values were related more to propagation characteristics than to the reaction itself. The extremely low E_a for the Fe-BaO$_2$ (80% Fe) mix is really a measure of the ease of heat transfer along the burning path.

Table I. Measured activation energies

Mix	E_a, cal
Fe-BaO$_2$	5700
S-BaO$_2$	3100
Fe - K$_2$Cr$_2$O$_7$	6900

Unfortunately, the Arrhenius equation has limited applicability to delay performance. For example, an old approximation based on the exponential dependence of k on T states that the reaction rate doubles for each 10 °C rise in temperature. This approximation is sometimes useful for gaseous reactions but not for delay mixes. In fact, if the Arrhenius relationship held for delay mixes, they would never meet military specifications which allow only a 10% maximum variation in delay time at ambient temperatures ranging from − 50 °C to as high as 75 °C. For an E_a of 25,000 cal, the burning rate at 75 °C would theoretically be about 9,000,000 times as fast as at − 50 °C.

Propagation mechanism

Much evidence supports the view that burning propagates by reignition from layer to layer along the burning path and therefore depends on thermal conductivity of the mix. The data for a Pb$_3$O$_4$-Si-Al mix in Table II, taken from McLain and Mayer[17], show the variation of burning rate with train cross section and packing density and indicate a planar transfer mechanism. Addition of inert materials such as kaolin, infusorial earth, and superfloss, with relatively low thermal conductivity, reduces the rate of heat transfer through the mix and slows the reactions. Conversely, Biddle and McLain[18] significantly increased burning rate by adding thermally conductive fine Cu and Ag powders to gasless delay mixes.

Other evidence appears in a U. S. Army Engineering Design Handbook[19] which states, "Loading Pressure - Burning rates of delay mixtures will decrease as the consolidation pressure increases." If this were true, the reaction involved would not be a true solid-solid reaction. Increased contact between reactants

Table II. Delay train diameter vs burning rate for 17.15-cm length

Nominal pipe size, inch	1/8	1/4	3/8
Train diameter, cm	0.716	0.963	1.60
Loading density, g/cm^3	1.72	1.86	2.03
Burning time, sec	6.1	6.5	6.7
Corrected for density, sec	7.2	7.1	6.7
Burning rate, cm/sec	2.38	2.42	2.51

would accelerate a true solid-solid reaction because it promotes the diffusion of crystal lattice components. To support the statement, the Handbook presents graphs for the 5:95 and 10:90 $B - BaCrO_4$ systems, shown here as dashed lines in Figures 1 and 2, to illustrate the decrease in burning rate with increase in loading density. However, when the burning rates are converted from in/sec to g/sec (plotted as solid lines), the picture changes. High consolidation pressures increase the reactant mass per unit length (g/cm). The mass burning rates are relatively constant with loading pressure, or increase with rising consolidation and level off as maximum density is approached.

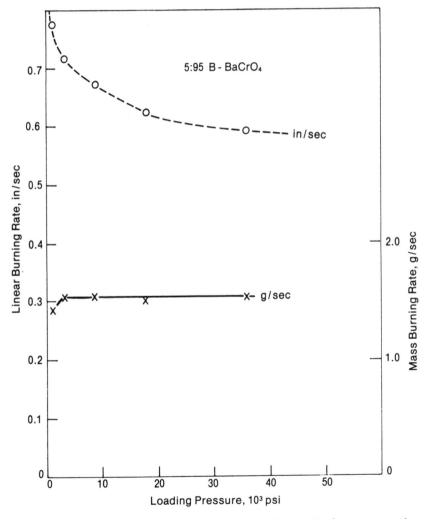

Figure 1. *Effect of loading pressure on* 5:95 B-BaCrO_4 *burning rate*[19].

The solid-line graphs allow the following conclusions:

The reaction is truly solid-solid.

The 10:90 system depends more on density than does the 5:95 system because it is more nearly stoichiometric; the excess, unreacted material contains less inert, insulating $BaCrO_4$ and more heat-conducting B.

Data are more scattered at very light consolidation pressures because contact and heat transfer between particles are poor and the rate of heat generation is too slow to overcome radiation losses.

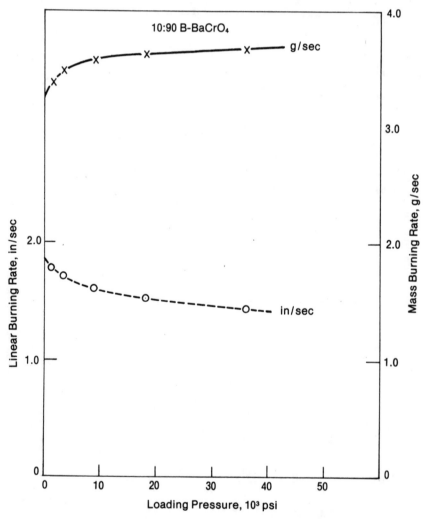

Figure 2. *Effect of loading pressure on* 10:90 B-BaCrO₄ *burning rate*[19].

Stoichiometry, heat of reaction, and burning rate

Stoichiometry, heat of reaction, and burning rate are interrelated. The relationship can be useful for interpreting experimental results. For example, a comparison of the graph of measured heats of reaction versus varied amount of a mix component with a graph of theoretical values calculated from heats of formation of possible reactions can help to single out the reaction that actually takes place.

PbO_2-Si system. Tests of the PbO_2-Si system illustrate this. Possible reactions are:

Si, %	Reaction
2.3	$Si + 4PbO_2 \rightarrow Pb_4SiO_6 + O_2$
3.1	$Si + 3PbO_2 \rightarrow SiO_2 + 3PbO + 3/2\ O_2$
4.8	$Si + 2PbO_2 \rightarrow Pb_2SiO_4$
6.0	$2Si + 3PbO_2 \rightarrow 2PbSiO_3 + Pb$
8.7	$Si + PbO_2 \rightarrow SiO_2 + Pb$
12.6	$3Si + 2PbO_2 \rightarrow SiO_2 + 2SiO + 2Pb$
16.1	$2Si + PbO_2 \rightarrow SiO_2 + 2Pb$
22.3	$3Si + PbO_2 \rightarrow Pb + Si + 2SiO$

Figure 3 shows graphs of the observed and calculated heats of reaction, ΔH. It can be seen that the observed heat of reaction reaches a maximum (which should correspond to a stoichiometric condition) near 10% Si, as does the calculated heat for the reaction, $PbO_2 + Si \rightarrow Pb + SiO_2$ (8.7% Si for stoichiometric proportions of reactants). A Q plot (Q is the amount of heat given off by a mixture containing 1 mol of oxidizer), shown in Figure 4, also flattens near 10% Si, indicating that this is the stoichiometric quantity of Si required to consume all the oxidizer.

A Q plot for the Pb_3O_4-Si system reaches a plateau above 20% Si, indicating a significantly different reaction. Measured burning rates for both these systems are maximum at or near a stoichiometric composition.

B-$BaCrO_4$ system. Figure 5 shows graphs of data, including burning rates, for the B-$BaCrO_4$ system[19]. The peaks in heat of reaction and burning rate and the edge of the Q plateau indicate a stoichiometric condition near 15% B.

The usual practice in delay train development has been to start with an intuitively stoichiometric composition and then vary it to achieve the desired

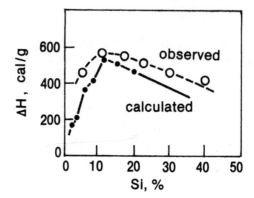

Figure 3. *Heats of reaction for* PbO$_2$-Si *system.*

burning rate. For example, in the B-BaCrO$_4$ system, the expected reaction is:

$$2B + 2BaCrO_4 \rightarrow B_2O_3 + 2BaO + Cr_2O_3$$

for which B constitutes slightly over 4% of the reactants. The intuitive mix would be in the ratio 5:95.

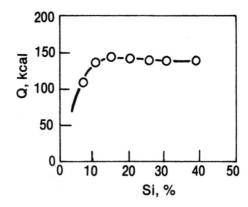

Figure 4. *Q-plot for* PbO$_2$-Si *system.*

However, Figure 5 indicates that the stoichiometric proportion of B is nearer 15%. This suggests that the active equation is:

$$4B + BaCrO_4 \rightarrow 4BO + Ba + Cr$$

for which B constitutes just over 14.5% of the reactants. The presence of this reaction may seem surprising because our minds are conditioned to a mild-temperature world. If we think of the reaction taking place at about 3000 °C, then the presence of the high temperature form BO and free metals (or vapors) becomes more reasonable. As a matter of fact, BO was found and isolated in the combustion zone of composite solid propellants containing B, and thermodynamic studies show BO to be more stable than B_2O_3 above 2000 °C. Also, metallic Ca has been detected during the burning of systems in which $CaCrO_4$ plays a role similar to that of $BaCrO_4$ in the present system.

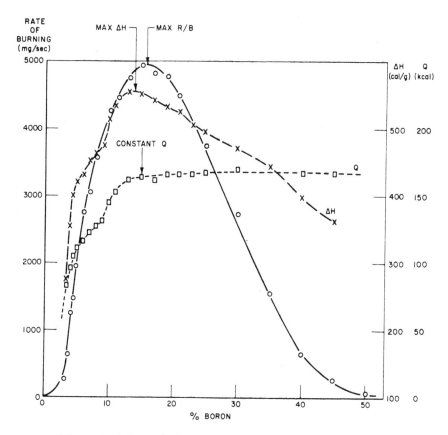

Figure 5. *Thermal characteristics of* B-$BaCrO_4$ *system*[19].

Effect of metal reductant on burning rate. The maximum burning rate in Figure 5 occurs at a somewhat higher reductant content than does the maximum heat of reaction. This was more or less true in some twenty other delay systems studied. The displacement is generally greater for metal reductants such as Fe, Sb, and Mn, and smaller for nonmetals such as S and C or metalloids such as B and Si.

This phenomenon points to the effect of heat transfer on columnar burning. Addition of a good heat conductor, such as a metal, may cause departure from stoichiometry, but may increase thermal conductivity sufficiently to cause a net increase in burning rate. Metals conduct heat better than do metalloids, and both are better conductors than nonmetallic oxidizing agents.

Such behavior also conforms to the heat-transfer mechanism of propagation postulated by Spice and Staveley and by Hill and his coworkers. Other experimental evidence also supports this postulate:

The smaller the heat of reaction, the more the peak in burning rate is displaced from the peak in heat of reaction.

The slope of the burning-rate curve is always steeper below the maximum (percent reductant below stoichiometric) than above the maximum (percent reductant above stoichiometric). The explanation is that the region below the maximum represents excess oxidizer, which is an inert diluent and heat insulator that retards burning. Addition of the thermally conductive reductant thus has a relatively large effect on accelerating the burning rate. Above the maximum, there is excess reductant. This maintains a relatively high burning rate in spite of the departure from stoichiometry as more reductant is added.

Practical application of burning-rate curve. Optimum delay performance is generally expected for stoichiometric compositions because they ignite and propagate more readily. However, sometimes design requirements may specify a slower (or faster) burning rate than that associated with strict stoichiometry.

Traditionally, the development engineer would decrease the amount of reductant. For example, the B-BaCrO$_4$ system of Figure 5, a mix with approximately 6% B would have a burning rate half the maximum. The rarely applied alternative of increasing the reductant to 30% to achieve the same lower burning rate is actually more desirable. The larger addition is more easily mixed, and slight departures from homogeneity would have less effect because the slope of this portion of the curve is not as steep.

Neither alternative is a *proper* solution since we would like to use all gasless delay systems at the experimentally determined stoichiometric composition. Only at that composition does the burning-rate curve round a peak so that slight inhomogeneities (local departures from stoichiometry) are less critical. This need not limit a given system to only one burning rate. As indicated previously, the addition of inert, thermally insulating ingredients will slow the reaction without upsetting stoichiometry, and addition of metal powder may successfully accelerate it.

However, good practice dictates that dilutions of a stoichiometric mix with inert matter should not exceed 4%, whether to retard or accelerate the burning rate. If the desired rate is not obtainable within these limits, another system should be used with a stoichiometric composition that yields a faster or slower burning rate as needed.

Gassy delays. Many so-called gasless delays are not very gasless. Even the relatively sluggish 20:10:70 W-KClO$_4$-BaCrO$_4$ system, with a nominal delay of 40 sec/in, produces KCl vapor. The more energetic 80:20 PbO-Si system, with a nominal delay of 2 sec/in, not only emits Pb vapor but, if burned in a sealed container, doubles its burning rate (halves the delay time). If gaslessness is indeed unattainable, why try so hard to attain it?

As a matter of fact, many gaseous systems are now in use. Notable among them are the K$_2$Cr$_2$O$_7$-B-Si delays developed in Australia by Andrew Scott. Typical oxidizer content is 90%, and different burning rates are produced by varying the B-Si ratio from 1:9 (slowest) to 10:0 (fastest).

This system proved to have a unique property, demonstrated in Figure 6[20]. At two distinct pressures, the burning rate is independent of temperature. This property can be exploited in practice by determining the volume of evolved gas and designing the container dimensions to produce either of the desirable pressure levels during burning. The pressure levels cannot be achieved exactly or held continuously, but approximating them will significantly reduce temperature dependence.

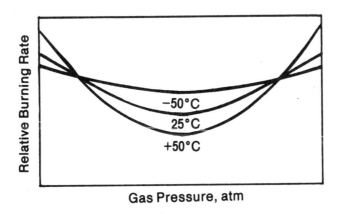

Figure 6. *Effect of gas pressure on* K$_2$Cr$_2$O$_7$-B-Si *burning rate*[20].

C.H. Miller[21] performed outstanding work with a coprecipitated B-$BaCrO_4$. The data, presented in Table III, show that the burning rate of the gassy delay varies with reduced pressure only if the mix is prepared mechanically. The burning rate of a coprecipitated mix is not affected. Perhaps this is the long-sought true antiaircraft delay.

Table III. Effect of reduced pressure on burning rate of B-$BaCrO_4$ delay compositions

Type of composition	Burning rate, sec/cm		
	Atmospheric pressure	25 mm Hg	5 mm Hg
Mechanical mix	0.840	0.963	0.972
Coprecipitated mix	1.433	1.442	1.436

The influence of pressure on the burning rate of delay mixes is of great importance to the explosives industry. Detonators with accurate and predictable delay times are necessary for good blasting procedures. These delays must be sealed, and any variation in the effectiveness of the seal will affect the delay time, sometimes with disastrous results. Puncture of a detonator can or leakage around the plug gives rise to erratic timing and invariably longer delays than under normal, sealed conditions.

Most cap manufacturers make two series of delay detonators, one with half-second increments, typically ranging from ½ to 5 sec, and the other with $25-35$-ms increments, designated by numbers 1 through 10. Some of the mixes used in these series are:

Millisecond Series	Half-second Series
PbO_2 - Si	BaO_2 - Se
Pb_3O_4 - Si	$KMnO_4$ - Sb
Pb_3O_4 - Si - Sb_2S_3	$BaCrO_4$ - Zr - Sb_2S_3
$BaCrO_4$ - PbO_2 - B	Fe - $KMnO_4$
	PbO - Si

J.S. Glasby[22] performed extensive tests of the effect of pressure up to 1400 psi and Figure 7 shows his results for two mixes in each of the series. Glasby summarized his work as follows:

In all cases the velocity of propagation increased with pressure reaching a limiting velocity at a critical pressure which was dependent on the composition.

The red lead-silicon compositions decreased again above 900—1000 psi and this effect was due to the pressure stabilization of the PbO moiety of the red lead and might explain, to some extent, the previously discovered fact that lead dioxide-silicon mixtures are far more regular in delay detonators than the corresponding red lead-silicon compositions.

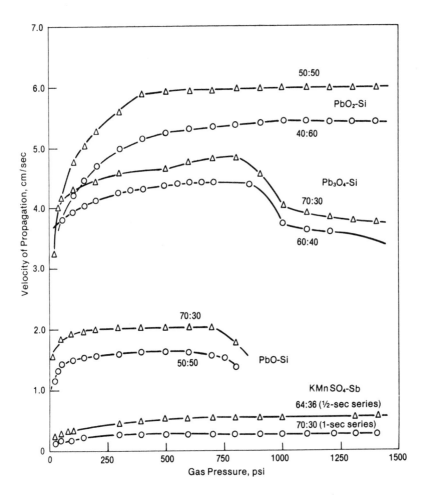

Figure 7. *Effect of pressure on gassy delay systems.*

Other gassy delay compositions have been mentioned by Cackett[23]. Notable in his list are:

>   Polyvinyl chloride - $BaNO_3$
>   Tetranitrocarbazole - KNO_3 and/or $Ba(NO_3)_2$
>   Tetranitro oxanilide - KNO_3 and/or $Ba(NO_3)_2$
>   Lactose - KNO_3.

RULES-OF THUMB FOR EMPIRICAL DELAY DESIGN

• To maximize burning rate for a given mix, use more than the stoichiometric proportion of reducing agent.

• To reduce the burning rate, decrease the heat of reaction. Two methods are:

>   Use a metal that produces less heat or one, for example, Mn, that reacts in several different ways depending on its proportion in the mix.

$$Mn + O_2 \rightarrow MnO_2$$
$$Mn + \tfrac{1}{2}O_2 \rightarrow MnO$$
$$2Mn + 3/2O_2 \rightarrow Mn_2O_3$$

>   Add an inert thermal insulator such as powdered glass, kieselguhr, fuller's earth, or superfloss.

• For mixes slower than 1 sec/in, use tubes with diameter ¼ inch or larger, whenever possible.

• Do not use tubes made of good heat conductors like brass or copper.

• Use a mix with as high a propagation index as possible for the desired burning rate.

• Keep close watch on:
>   *Particle sizes* of constituent powders
>   *Size* and *chemical nature* of guest particles
>   *Adsorbed gases* on particle surfaces
>   *Loading* method and pressure
>   Mix *homogeneity*
>   *Temperature* and *type of ignition*
>   *Mix type* - low gas or gassy
>   *Humidity* during mixing and loading.

NEW DEVELOPMENTS

New mixes have appeared during the last ten years. Among these are:

Zr-MoO_3, 1 to 0.33 and 2.0 to 6.3 in/sec, W.H.
Colburn, Jr. U.S. Patent 3,703,144

MnO_2-Fe-Si, C.A. Lipscomb

Pb_3O_4-Si-NaF, millisecond delay detonators

ZrB_2 and HfB_2, Russian, *Chem. Abs.* 81 93605 m

Sb-FeO-$KClO_4$ (35:43:22), ½-sec caps, German Offen
2,416,920

MnO_2-Si (83:12) plus 2% Portland cement, castable
40-sec/in delay, Belgian Patent 817,842 (1974)

$KClO_4$-Fe (76:22)

Fe_2O_3-Al-B-PbSn alloy-Se-Snowfroth, cap delay for
use under humid conditions, *Chem. Abs.* 86
57654W

*Arts and sciences are not cast in a mould, but are
formed and perfected by degrees, by often handling and
polishing, as bears leisurely lick their cubs into form.*

Montaigne

Chapter V

REFERENCES

1. British Patent 6159 (1831).
2. U.S. Patent 2,457,860 (1949).
3. U.S. Patent 1,805,214 (1931).
4. U.S. Patent 2,696,429 (1954).
5. U.S. Patent 2,643,946 (1953).
6. Spice, J.E. and Staveley, L.A.K., *J. Soc. Chem. Ind.* **68**, 313-39 (1949).
7. Hill, R.A.W., Sutton, L.E., Temple, R.B., and White, A., *Research* **3**, 569-576 (1950).
8. Hill, R.A.W. and Cottrell, T.L., "Studies of Combustion Waves," in *4th Symposium (International) on Combustion*, Williams and Wilkins, Baltimore, 1953.
9. Henkin, H. and McGill, R., *Ind. and Eng. Chem.* **44**, 1391 (1952).
10. Nakahara, S., *J. Ind. Explos. Soc.* (Japan) **21**, 363-374 (1961).
11. Boys, S.F. and Corner, J.R., *Proc R. Soc.* London, Series A **197**, 90 (1949).
12. Booth, F., *Trans. Faraday Soc.* **47**, 277 (1953).
13. McLain, J.H., *Development of the Fuze, Grenade, Igniting, M201*, TDMR 881, Edgewood Arsenal, Md., 1944.
14. Rose, James E., *Flame Propagation Parameters of Pyrotechnic Delay and Ignition Compositions*, IHMR 71-168, Naval Ordnance Station, Indian Head, Md., 1971.
15. Johnson, Duane M., RDTR 56, U.S. Naval Ammunition Depot, Crane, Ind., 1965.
16. McLain, J.H. and McClure, M.D., *Effect of Phase Change in Solid-Solid Reactions*, Report WCDC 6667, Chemical Research and Development Laboratories, Edgewood Arsenal, Md., 1968.
17. McLain, J.H. and Mayer, S., *Delay Trains for Use in Floating Smoke Pots*, TDMR 732, Edgewood Arsenal, Md., 1943.
18. Biddle, H.O. and McLain, J.H., Senior Thesis, Washington College, Chestertown, Md., 1970.
19. *Engineering Design Handbook, Military Pyrotechnic Series, Part I*, "Theory and Application," AMCP 706-185, U.S. Army Materiel Command, April 1967 (data from Werbel, B. and Lopatin, S., Report 2477, Picatinny Arsenal, Dover, N.J., 1958).
20. Private communication from Sidney Howlett, July 1971.
21. Miller, C.H. and Benge, R.J., *Development of Initiating and Igniferous Materials for Use in Extreme Conditions*, WAA/189/10, E.R.D.E., Waltham Abbey, Essex, England, and British Patent 1,333,551 (1978).
22. Glasby, J.S., *The Effect of Ambient Pressure on the Velocity of Propagation of Half-Second and Short Delay Compositions*, Imperial Chemical Industries, Nobel Division, Ardeer, Scotland (private communication, 1961).
23. Cackett, J.C., *Monograph on Pyrotechnic Compositions*, Royal Armament Research and Development Establishment, Fort Halstead, Seven Oaks, Kent, England, 1965 (RESTRICTED).

Chapter VI

SMOKES

Pyrotechnically generated smokes were developed largely for military purposes but their use has broadened to include agricultural and other civilian applications.

MILITARY SCREENING SMOKES

Modern military smokes evolved from the mixtures of metal powders with halogenated organic compounds patented in 1920 by Captain Henri Berger of the French army.

HC Type A

The standard mixture used by the U.S. prior to 1941 was called HC smoke, later designated Type A, and had the following composition:

> Zn dust
> Hexachloroethane (C_2Cl_6)
> $CaCO_3$
> NH_4Cl
> $KClO_4$

It was used in a variety of munitions, including the M8 grenade, shell canisters, the M1 pot, and the M4 floating smoke pot. The primary reaction:

$$3Zn + C_2Cl_6 \rightarrow 3ZnCl_2 + 2C + heat$$

gave a dense, dark-gray smoke but the mix became too hot and burned too fast.

Addition of NH_4Cl reduced the burning rate and heat output while consuming heat in dissociation:

$$NH_4Cl + heat \rightarrow NH_3 + HCl$$

The gas products of dissociation then recombined to reform NH_4Cl, which enhanced the total obscuring power (T.O.P.). The reduction in burning rate also improved field effectiveness. If the burning munition gives off too much heat, the hot gases rise too quickly in a pillar of smoke, especially at low wind speeds, instead of spreading laterally as desired to protect ground troops.

$KClO_4$ was added to oxidize the C produced by the primary reaction and thus whiten the smoke. Measurements proved white smoke to be more effective than gray smoke as a screening agent, especially during the brighter daylight hours. Extra heat generated by the oxidation reaction could be compensated for by cooling additions of more NH_4Cl.

Addition of $CaCO_3$ also helped to cool the smoke:

$$CaCO_3 + heat \rightarrow CaO + CO_2$$

but its main function was to neutralize acid formed during mixing or storage and thus prevent premature ignition.

In spite of the $CaCO_3$, the HC Type A smoke gained a deservedly bad reputation because it started fires in warehouses or in transit. A few drops of moisture that penetrated the container could ignite the munition with little warning. The author saw a grenade self-ignite after it had rested on snow for about seven minutes.

HC Type B

In 1941, all Type A smokes were replaced by the *British Smoke Mix* composed of:

> ZnO
> Hexachloroethane
> $CaSi_2$

This Type B smoke was safer than Type A in storage but still gassed badly if exposed to moisture, as shown in Table I. Also, $CaSi_2$ is not the safest material to grind and handle. However, the idea of putting Zn into the mix in the form of a stable oxide to be reduced only when necessary was excellent and warranted further exploitation.

Table I. Evolved gas due to moisture in 2-inch smoke bomb
(filled by MacDonald Chemicals, Waterloo; tested by Donald Inspection, Ltd.,
Montreal, Canada)

	I %	II %	III %	IV %
Phosphene, acetylene	0	0.1	0	0.7
Carbon dioxide	0.1	0.3	0	0
Carbon monoxide	0	0	0	0
Oxygen	4.9	2.0	12.2	1.4
Hydrogen	55.1	70.5	17.2	67.2
Nitrogen	39.9	27.1	69.6	30.7
Methane, etc.	0	0	0	0
Total, cm³/hr	50	65	20	120

HC Type C

Consequently, early in 1942, the author sought more stable reducing agents than $CaSi_2$ which would still reduce ZnO. An obvious one was Al, which was also relatively cheap and plentiful. The developmental sequence that resulted in the successful use of Al is an illuminating case history.

It began with a stoichiometric mix containing ZnO, atomized Al, and hexachloroethane. The reaction was:

$$2Al + 3ZnO + C_2Cl_6 \rightarrow Al_2O_3 + 3ZnCl_2 + 2C$$

A grenade loaded with this mix produced a dense gray smoke but burned in about 15 − 20 sec and became so hot it melted. The smoke was too fast, too hot, and too dark.

Usual remedies were not attractive. NH_4Cl additions would cut down the burning rate and heat, but might adversely affect storage stability. Something like $CaCO_3$ would dilute the smoke. An oxidizer of the $KClO_4$ type would whiten the smoke, but would also make it burn even faster and hotter. Therefore, another idea was tried, based on a reversible Zn reaction.

Under ordinary conditions, Zn metal reduces CO by the reaction:

$$Zn + CO \rightarrow ZnO + C$$

which releases 57.9 kcal/g mol as heat. It also has a large negative entropy change of 45.25 cal/mol°K, which implied that the reaction would reverse at a sufficiently high temperature to:

$$ZnO + C \;\rightarrow\; CO + Zn$$

with the absorption of 57.9 kcal/g mol. This is the standard reaction for smelting Zn. The temperature required for the reversal equals the heat of reaction divided by the change in entropy:

$$T = 57,900/45.25 = 1280\,°K \text{ or approximately } 1000\,°C$$

Since the new smoke mix certainly became this hot, it seemed that ZnO could both oxidize C (whiten the gray) and cool the smoke. Accordingly, the following scheme was worked out (heats of formation in kcal/g mol are -84.33 for ZnO, -390 for Al_2O_3, and -26.42 for CO):

$$
\begin{aligned}
2Al + 3ZnO &\rightarrow Al_2O_3 + 3Zn + 137 \text{ kcal/g mol}\\
3Zn + C_2Cl_6 &\rightarrow 3ZnCl_2 + 2C\\
2C + 2ZnO &\rightarrow 2Zn + 2CO - 116 \text{ kcal/g mol}\\
2Zn + 2/3\,C_2Cl_6 &\rightarrow 2ZnCl_2 + 4/3\,C\\
4/3\,C + 4/3\,ZnO &\rightarrow 4/3\,Zn + 4/3\,CO - 77 \text{ kcal/g mol}\\
4/3\,Zn + 4/9\,C_2Cl_6 &\rightarrow 4/3\,ZnCl_2 + 8/9\,C
\end{aligned}
$$

and so on until the ZnO and C_2Cl_6 are depleted. The reactions involving ZnO withdraw $116 + 77 - 137 = 56$ kcal/g mol of heat from the quantity released by the primary reaction involving only Zn and C_2Cl_6. The summation of the above six-step reaction sequence and the relative weights and approximate percentages of the reactants are:

$$
\begin{aligned}
2Al + 19/3\,ZnO &+ 19/9\,C_2Cl_6 \rightarrow\\
&Al_2O_3 + 19/3\,ZnCl_2 + 10/3\,CO + 8/9C\\
54\text{ g} &+ 515.4\text{ g} + 499.8\text{ g} = 1069.2\text{ g}\\
5\% &+ 48.5\% + 46.5\% = 100\%
\end{aligned}
$$

This gives a constant ratio of 515.4 g of ZnO to 499.8 g of C_2Cl_6, approximately 51% to 49%. Continuation of the scheme to decrease the exothermic nature of the reaction does not change this ratio, but merely decreases the overall percentage of Al. In other words, the higher the % Al, the greater the heat of reaction, and vice versa. If the reaction rate is due to the amount of heat, as suggested by Cottrell and Hill[1], then the burning time of a grenade with Type C mix can be adjusted to duplicate the Type A burning time by reduction of the % Al to take out the extra heat generated by the Al-ZnO reaction.

As shown above, a 5%-Al mix corresponds to six reaction steps and the removal of 56 kcal/g mol of heat. This was believed to be too much cooling, so the sequence was calculated for just four steps. The summation is:

$$2Al + 5ZnO + 5/3\ C_2Cl_6 \rightarrow 5\ ZnCl_2 + Al_2O_3 + 2CO + 4/3\ C$$

and the mix would contain 6.3% Al. This amount made the reaction a little too hot and fast. Adjusting the Al to 137/193 of the full-step increment from 5.0% to 6.3%, i.e., to 5.9%, would give approximately the required standard burning time of 2.0−2.5 min.

Twenty-five grenades loaded with 95.1 parts of a premixed 51:49 ZnO-C_2Cl_6 formulation and 5.9 parts of Al had an average burning time of 2 min 20 sec and varied no more than +20 or −19 sec. Smoke quality was excellent, color was light gray to white, and the solid residue was only half that from the HC Type B smoke mix. For production mixes, which were less homogeneous, the Al content had to be increased to 6.2% to compensate for slow burning in Al-deficient regions.

It is not too important that the reaction-heat analysis singled out the 5.9%-Al composition which gave exactly the desired burning time. This may have been attributable to luck as well as calculation. The significance of the analysis is that it provided a good starting point and the basic understanding of the process that later helped in the quick solution of production problems. A strictly empirical approach might have taken longer with less assurance of eventual success and ultimate understanding.

HC Type D

Not long after the development of HC Type C, the same analytic approach produced a satisfactory mix for a screening smoke requiring the use of hexachlorbenzene, C_6Cl_6. The large number of C atoms in the C_6Cl_6 molecule presented a special problem. It was not possible to reduce the Al content enough to oxidize most of the C and whiten the smoke without simultaneously reducing the burning rate below the level needed to make a good cloud. The mix had the specified burning time, but the smoke was always darker than desired.

HC Type E

The method used for HC Type C was also used to develop and standardize a carbon tetrachloride (CCl_4) formulation. Although the CCl_4 volatility presented significant problems, it also had some advantages, especially in long, narrow munitions cases that could be hermetically sealed. The HC Type E mix had the consistency of heavy paste and was extruded into munitions like toothpaste from a tube. It was by far the best smoke filler for the M77 bomb.

HC Types FH and GC

For certain naval operations, nonfloating smokepots were being loaded with a slightly modified HC Type A mixture enclosed in a hermetically sealed can sealed with a tear strip. Although these gave excellent smoke, their burning temperature was quite high. In addition to the risk of setting fire to nearby objects on shipboard, the flaming made the screen-laying craft a visible target to shore batteries or other hostile fire. Moisture-induced spontaneous ignition had also been encountered. The burning temperature was $1020\,°C$ so that HC Type C, with an even higher burning temperature of $1160\,°C$, was not a suitable replacement.

Two new mixes were developed:

Type FH	Type GC
Mn 13.0%	Mn 8.5%
ZnO 37.8%	ZnO 42.5%
C_2Cl_6 49.2%	CCl_4 49.0%
Flame temp. $884\,°C$	Flame temp. $723\,°C$

They gave a very white smoke cloud of satisfactory volume and screening power and, more importantly, were invisible 20 feet away at night.

During this work, TiO_2 was tested as a substitute for ZnO in the HC Type C mix to compare the reaction products, $TiCl_4$ versus $ZnCl_2$, as white-smoke generators. Although the burning temperature of the TiO_2 mix was not as high as that of the unmodified HC Type C, it exceeded that of the Type FH in which Mn replaces Al. The TiO_2 smoke also had less volume and a yellowish tinge. Heat analysis of the reactions, shown in Table II, correlated with the experimentally observed differences in burning temperature and resulted in an early solution.

Table II. Heats of smoke-mix reactions

Mix	Reaction	Heat, cal/g
Type C	$2Al + 3ZnO + C_2Cl_6 \rightarrow 3ZnCl_2 + Al_2O_3 + 2C$	644.6
TiO_2	$4Al + 3TiO_2 + 2C_2Cl_6 \rightarrow 3TiCl_4 + 2Al_2O_3 + 4C$	598.0
Type FH	$3Mn + 3ZnO + C_2Cl_6 \rightarrow 3ZnCl_2 + 3MnO + 2C$	365.0

German smoke mix

Analysis of the contents of a German Nb39 hand grenade indicated the following probable original composition:

Zn	37.4 %
Mg	1.85%
ZnO	14.3 %
C_2Cl_6	46.2 %

When burned, the mix produced a relatively white cloud, probably due to oxidation of the C to CO by ZnO as with the HC Type C mix.

Recent smoke mixes

Two new pyrotechnic screening smokes have appeared in recent years. One, by Douda and Tanner[2], uses a novel agent, transcinnamic acid:

$KClO_3$	29.0%
Sucrose	12.0%
Transcinnamic acid	47.5%
$NaHCO_3$	6.5%

The other comes from the famous old French fireworks firm of Ruggieri and contains:

$KClO_3$	23.33%
Lactose	23.33%
Neoprene	46.67%
Cobalt octoate	2.0 %

It is said to emit a voluminous white smoke.

Oil-based screening smokes

In oil-based smokes, a burning mix generates oil droplets of sufficiently small size to create a good white screening smoke. Comings and Johnston did most of the research work on this type of smoke during World War II. Development details have been described elsewhere; only a representative composition will be given here:

	Screening		Proportion	
	Mesh	% Pass	%	
NH_4NO_3	− 60	95 min.	77	
	−100	15 min.		
	−200	50 max.		
Charcoal	−200	85 min.	16	
	−325	75 min.		
KNO_3	−60	99 min.	3-5	(as needed to control
	−170	20 max.		burning rate)
Fuel oil			2	

This mix was pressed into the lower compartment of a two-compartment container and ignited by flash from a fuze through a center hole in the top compartment. The flash struck first-fire (FFB 242) material pressed into the body of the compacted mix. The upper compartment contained Diol 55.

During operation, hot gases from the burning mix traveled through the tube and melted a Woods-metal plug in a small hole at the base of the tube. This opening allowed the oil to drip out into the hot gas stream to be vaporized into a large volume of dense white smoke.

The great advantage of oil smoke is freedom from toxicity, which allows it to be used for indefinitely long periods to screen friendly troops. All $ZnCl_2$ smokes cause headaches if personnel are exposed to screening quantities for more than 20 minutes.

MILITARY COLORED SMOKES

The colored smokes used by the U.S. during World War II, and still in use, were developed at Edgewood Arsenal, Maryland, early in 1942 by Dr. Sidney J. Magram and Lieutenant D.H. West, in close association with Major W.P. Munro, Captain J.C. Driskell, and Sergeant O.C. Tubbs. The problem looked formidable at first: build a fire in a container and sublime from an intimate mix a highly flammable hydrocarbon dye. Yet, within a month preliminary test grenades were being burned and within another month the standardized M16 grenade was available in red, yellow, green, blue, and violet.

The smoke formulation consisted of a fuel and a dye mixed together and pressed into a can. The fuel was a stoichiometric mix of S and $KClO_3$, which reacted as follows:

$$3S + 2KClO_3 \rightarrow 3SO_2 + 2KCl$$

and $NaHCO_3$ which served as a coolant, flame suppressor, and alkalizing agent. For safety reasons, the $KClO_3$ and $NaHCO_3$ were always mixed together first before addition of the S and dye.

About a year and a half later, an improved version was developed and eventually became the standardized M18 grenade, available in four colors. The M18 differed from the M16 in construction rather than mix. In the M16, a column burned from end to end like a cigarette. The mix in the M18 can was pressed around a metal mandrel so that burning was confined to a ring around the inner surface of a cylinder.

Typical mixes for the M18 grenade were as shown in Table III.

Table III. Compositions for M18 colored smoke grenade

Color	Dye %	NaHCO₃ %	KClO₃ %	S %
Green	40.0	24	25.9	10.1
Red	40.0	18	30.2	11.8
Violet	42.0	18	28.8	11.2
Yellow	38	31.5	22.0	8.5

The $KClO_3$-S ratio was kept constant at 2.55:1 to sustain stoichiometry, but the amount of coolant was varied up to 40% of the total fuel mix for green, 30% for red, 31% for violet, and 50% for yellow, depending on the dye's heat of sublimation and sensitivity to pyrolitic decomposition. Thousands of tons of these mixes have been used in munitions with excellent results.

Table IV lists current U.S. Army standard colored smoke mixes, including some in which S was replaced by other combustibles for different applications as a result of later developments.

Table IV. U.S. Army standard colored smoke mixes

Designation	Colors	Composition
M3, M4 (green only)	Green, yellow	KClO₃-lactose-MgCO₃-dye
M18, M22AZ	Red, green	KClO₃-S-NaHCO₃-dye
M23Al	Red, yellow	KClO₃-sucrose-dye
M23Al	Green	KClO₃-sucrose-KHCO₃-dye
M23Al	Violet	KClO₃-S-NaHCO₃-dye
XM64	Green	KClO₃-lactose-nitrocellulose-dye

The U.S. Navy does not use any colored smoke mixes containing S. A typical Navy formulation contains:

Component	%
KClO₃	30
Sucrose	20
NaHCO₃	10
Dye	40
Silocel	1
Cabosil	1

Other military colored smoke compositions, listed in Table V, are available but not standardized.

Table V. Additional military colored smoke mixes

Color	Constituents	%	Color	Constituents	%
Yellow	Auramine O	38.0	Black	$KClO_4$	55.0
	$NaHCO_3$	28.5		Anthracene	45.0
	$KClO_3$	24.1			
	S	9.4			
Yellow	β-naphthaleneazo-		Violet	1-methylamino-	
	dimethylaniline	50.0		anthraquinone	18.0
	$KClO_3$	30.0		1-4 diamino-2,3-	
	Sucrose	20.0		dihydroanthra-	
				quinone	26.0
Red	9-diethylamino-			$NaHCO_3$	14.0
	rosindone	48.0		$KClO_3$	30.2
	$KClO_3$	26.0		S	11.8
	Sucrose	26.0			
Red	1-methylamino-		Green	Auramine O	18.0
	anthraquinone	42.5		1-4 di-p-toluidino-	
	$KClO_3$	27.4		anthraquinone	28.3
	$NaHCO_3$	19.5		$NaHCO_3$	24.0
	S	10.6		$KClO_3$	25.9
				S	10.1
Orange	α-aminoanthra-				
	quinone	24.6	Blue	1,4-dimethylamino-	
	Auramine O	16.4		anthraquinone	50.0
	$NaHCO_3$	23.0		$KClO_3$	25.0
	$KClO_3$	25.9		Sucrose	25.0
	S	10.1			
Orange	1-amino-8-chloro-		Plaid	Cutty Sark red	20.0
	anthraquinone	39.0		Gretna green	20.0
	Auramine O	6.0		Mac indigo blue	20.0
	$NaHCO_3$	24.0		Scotia sucrose	20.0
	$KClO_3$	22.3		Caledonian chlorate	20.0
	S	8.7		(For McLain tartan only)	

$KClO_3$-S REACTION

Details of the $KClO_3$-S reaction are of interest in smoke generation because so many mixes contain these substances. It has been assumed that the reaction takes place in two steps. First, the chlorate decomposes:

$$2KClO_3 \rightarrow 2KCl + 3O_2$$

then the S oxidizes:

$$3O_2 + 3S \rightarrow 3SO_2$$

However, differential thermal analysis[3] has proved this to be a false assumption (see Figure 1).

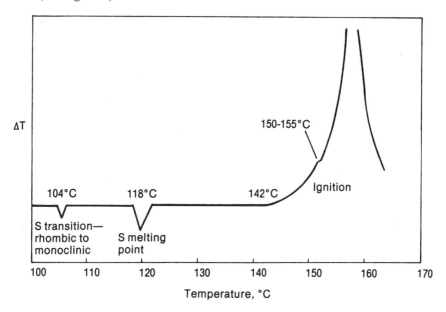

Figure 1. *Schematic thermogram of* $KClO_3$-S *system*[3].

Uncatalyzed $KClO_3$ does not decompose until after it melts at 368 °C. The commonly reported decomposition temperature is 400 °C. Even when catalyzed with MnO_2, CuO, or Co_2O_3, it does not decompose until 200 − 220 °C. Shidlovskiy[4] has reported attempts to increase the burning rate of chlorate compositions with additions of decomposition catalysts that actually decreased the burning rates.

The true reaction sequence is believed to be as follows. As the mixture is heated, the S undergoes a crystal transition from S_8 rhombic to S_8 monoclinic, then melts to an S_8 liquid. With continued heating, the liquid S_8 molecules break into S_3-S_2-S_5 fragments (λ -to- π liquid-liquid transition). The λ - to- π transition of recrystallized and purified S has been found to start at 140 °C. The S_3-S_2-S_5 fragments more easily penetrate the loosened $KClO_3$ lattice, or at least erode it, and create fissures and other imperfections. The ensuing reaction emits heat which creates more imperfections and reactive sites, which continue to increase until ignition occurs. The reaction rate should be fastest when the S_3 fragments are at peak concentration, at 159.1 °C according to West[5]. Ignition or explosion should occur just prior to this temperature.

This is a good point at which to recognize the importance of $KClO_3$ which can hardly be overstated. In many formulations, the fuel may vary from S to lactose to sucrose and other compounds, but $KClO_3$ is the uniquely requisite oxidizer. It is the finest low temperature oxidizer in our arsenal of reagents. Nothing else compares with it and the long search for an alternative has been in vain. Its importance as a low temperature oxidizer is also apparent in the fireworks industry. If another oxidizer is used, the higher burning temperature bleaches out the color of stars, especially blue ones.

TOXIC SMOKES

Smokes have been developed to kill insects and other pests. Some generate aerosols similar to those of the oil-based military screening smokes.

Insecticides

Heath and coworkers[6] at Porton, England, sublimed DDT (1:1 bis p-chlorphenyl 2:2:2 trichlorethane) and Gammexane (8-isomer of benzene hexachloride) from the following composition with at least 75% efficiency:

$KClO_3$	19%
Sucrose	23%
Insecticide	58%

In practice, about 2% MgO was added to fix any HCl that might evolve during high temperature storage. Such efficiencies in DDT generation from an intimate mixture are remarkable because DDT begins to lose HCl at 180 °C and the commercial grade is even more susceptible to decomposition. Heath also raised the efficiencies with 54.9% DDT mixtures to as high as 90% by replacing the sucrose in the fuel with urea and thiourea.

Another British insecticide formulation consists of:

$KClO_3$	16.5%
Thiourea	11.5%
Lingane	60%
Mineral filler	9%
MgO	3%

Other chemical insecticides such as chloracetophenone and CS have also been used in intimate mixtures, posing difficult design problems because of their susceptibility to pyrolytic decomposition.

Rodenticides

Toward the end of World War II, the U. S. Fish and Wildlife Service and the U. S. Department of Agriculture requested development of a pyrotechnic device to control gophers, prairie dogs, and woodchucks. The Berger HC Smoke Mix was the first to succeed, but had shortcomings in that freshly turned earth adsorbed significant amounts of the toxic gas. Dr. Sidney Magram found a satisfactory solution to the problem with the Magram candle, a mixture of KNO_3 and C, carefully balanced to generate large quantities of CO. CO gas is extremely lethal and not as readily adsorbed as previously used toxic gases.

Ellern[7] has suggested an SO_2 generator as a possible rodenticide, using a balanced mixture of two reactions:

$$KClO_4 + 2S \rightarrow 2SO_2 + KCl$$
$$CuSO_4 + 2S \rightarrow 2SO_2 + CuS$$

However, SO_2 is easily and rapidly adsorbed on fresh earth and would not be as effective as the CO of the Magram candle.

SPECIAL SMOKES

Smoke puffs

Colored smokes with a central burster-igniter have been used to produce smoke puffs for spotting rounds of exceptionally quick times. Another novel and very fast-acting composition is a 70:30 or 80:20 mixture of $KMnO_4$ and powdered Mg.

Black Smokes

One very good black smoke contains ZnO-Al-C_6Cl_6 and anthracene or naphthalene to cool it down. Ellern[8] gives the black-smoke formulations: C_2Cl_6, Fe powder, and Mg; and C_2Cl_6, Mg, anthracene, and naphthalene. T. Shimizu[9] reports good results with the black-smoke compositions in Table VI.

Table VI. Black-smoke compositions

	%		%		%		%
$KClO_4$	56	$KClO_3$	44	C_2Cl_6	62	$KClO_4$	53
S	11	Sb_2S_3	24	Mg	15	Anthracene	37.5
Anthracene	33	Naphthalene	26	Naphthalene	23	Hemp coal	3.0
		Rice starch	6	or anthracene		Rice starch	6.5

Fireworks smokes

Shimizu also gives the compositions in Tables VII and VIII for fireworks smoke displays.

Table VII. Chlorate color smokes

Color	$KClO_3$	Dye		Wheat flour
Red	25%	Rhodamine B	24%	15%
		Para red	36%	
Blue	28%	Methylene blue	17%	15%
		Indigo	40%	
Green	28%	Auramine	10%	15%
		Methylene blue	17%	
		Indigo	30%	
Violet	26%	Indigo	22%	15%
		Rhodamine B	16%	
		Para red	21%	

Table VIII. White and yellow smokes

Color	Composition	%
Sulfur white smoke	KNO_3	48.5
	Sulfur	48.5
	Realgar (As_2S_3)	3.0
Realgar yellow smoke	KNO_3	25
	S	16
	As_2S_3	59
Zinc white smoke	ZnO	22
	Zn	28
	C_2Cl_6	50

Quasipyrotechnic smokes

Aerially delivered smokes such as FS (chlorsulfonic acid) and FM (titanium tetrachloride) have not been discussed because they are not pyrotechnically generated. The same holds true for the various WP (white phosphorus) smoke devices that use a high explosive burster. One red phosphorus floating smoke marker, which can be considered quasipyrotechnic, is composed of:

	%
Red phosphorus	50
MnO_2	40
ZnO	8
Boiled linseed oil	3

If 7−8% Mg powder is added to this composition, it can be used as a combination day-night signal.

SAFETY

Screening smokes such as HC Types A and B are subject to autoignition if moisture enters the mix because powdered Zn metal and $CaSi_2$ react with water. The Type C mix is much safer throughout mixing, loading, and storage. All of these mixes have been ignited upon setback in artillery rounds, but setback ignition can be prevented for Type C if consolidation pressure is high enough during loading.

Type C is best mixed by tumbling in double-cone blenders or their equivalent. Although many tons were mixed without incident in dough mixers during World War II, tramp metal did cause ignition in a 500-lb batch, causing a considerable smoke problem.

Colored smokes which use $KClO_3$ (all military formulations) should contain an alkali to neutralize any acid that might form. For mixing safety, the $NaHCO_3$ or $MgCO_3$ should always be premixed with the $KClO_3$ before addition of the fuel and dye. Mixers have exploded during mixing and discharge. The force is considerable and can seriously harm personnel and facilities. Paradoxically, the pressed colored smoke mix in its container has never been known to explode, although minor ruptures of a side seam or lid have occurred.

Pressing is probably the most dangerous time of the loading operation. Ignition of unconsolidated or partially consolidated mix while confined by the press ram has created high-order explosions and fragmentation of the mold which caused fatalities. Fires have also started on vibrating screens with both sulfur and sugar mixes.

During studies of the effect of small amounts of metal salts on $KClO_3$ reactivity, 2 mol % of Cu^{2+} incorporated into the $KClO_3$ lattice caused room-temperature detonations of a mix of the doped $KClO_3$ with sulfur.

Visions I no longer see
And smoke is only smoke to me
                                        R. C. Rogers

Chapter VI

REFERENCES

1. Hill, R.A.W. and Cottrell, T.L., "Studies of Combustion Waves," in *4th Symposium (International) on Combustion,* Williams and Wilkins, Baltimore, 1953.

2. Douda, B.E. and Tanner, J.E., U.S. Patent 4,032,374 (1977).

3. McLain, J.H. and Lewis, D.V., *Effect of Phase Change on Solid-Solid Reactions,* Report WCDC 6465, Chemical Research and Development Laboratories, Edgewood Arsenal, Md., 1965.

4. Shidlovskiy, A.A., *Foundations of Pyrotechnics,* Report FTD-II-63-758 (trans. DDC AD 602 687), Air Force Systems Command, Wright-Patterson AFB, Ohio, 1964.

5. West, E.D., *J. Am. Chem. Soc.* **81,** 29 (1959).

6. Bateman, E.W. and Heath, G.D., *J. Soc. Chem. Ind.* **66,** 325 (1947) and Heath, G.D., **68,** 41 (1949).

7. Ellern, H., Kowarsky, I., and Olander. D.E., U.S. Patent 2,842,477 (1958).

8. Ellern, H., *Military and Civilian Pyrotechnics,* Chemical Publishing Co., New York, 1968.

9. Lancaster, R., Shimizu, T., Butler, R.E.A., and Hall, R.G., *Fireworks Principles and Practice,* Chemical Publishing Co., New York, 1972.

Chapter VII

LIGHT

And God said, Let there be light: and there was light.
Genesis 1:14

Illumination—spiritual, mental, and physical—has long been a quest of mankind. Darkness has always been something to be feared and dispelled. No book on pyrotechnics would be complete without a chapter on light (or flares).

Parade torches were probably the earliest pyrotechnic flares and the ancestors of today's railway and truck fusees. Others with a long, distinguished history include types such as aircraft signals and Very flares shot from special pistols. Although all pyrotechnic flares emit light, some (illuminants) are designed to make their surroundings visible, while others (signals) are designed primarily to be visible themselves. We will treat the two types separately according to their primary purpose.

ILLUMINATION

World War I gave impetus to the development of illuminating flares. Shidlovskiy[1] cites the following composition used at that time:

$Ba(NO_3)_2$	76%
Al dust	10%
Al powder	8%
S	4%
Castor oil	2%

In a flare with a 10.5-cm diameter and 2.3-g/cm^3 pressed density, it burned at 1.7 mm/sec with a luminous efficiency of 11,600 candle-sec/g. (Luminous efficiency $L_O = It/m$, where I is the light intensity in candles, t is the burning time in seconds, and m is the mass in grams. Thus, a 400-g flare that burns with an average intensity of 100,000 candles for 2 minutes has a luminous efficiency of 100,000 x 120/400 = 30,000 candle-sec/g.) The U.S. Navy 5-inch round, which released a parachute flare, dated from that period.

During World War II, the author helped to develop an illuminating shell for the 4.2-inch mortar, a direct discendant of the Navy round, which also ejected a canister attached to a parachute. The flare contained $Ba(NO_3)_2$, Al or an Al-Mg alloy, S, and a boiled linseed oil binder, and had a luminous efficiency of 15,000 candle-sec/g, bright enough to make a magazine readable on a moonless, starless night. The present filler for the 4.2-inch illuminating shell contains:

NaNO$_3$	45%
Mg	45%
Polyvinyl chloride	2%
Laminac	8%

(Laminac is composed of 97.9% 4116 compound, 1.5% Lupersol, and 0.6% Nuodex.) The filler for the 81-mm mortar illuminating round is:

NaNO$_3$	36%
Mg	55%
Laminac	9%

which has a luminous efficiency of over 48,000 candle-sec/g (625 g burns at an intensity of over 500,000 candles for more than 60 sec).

Photoflash flares

Other World War II pyrotechnic illuminants had intensities in the millions of candles for short periods and served as photoflash devices for nighttime aerial photography. The first versions contained $Ba(NO_3)_2$, Al or an Al-Mg alloy, and $KClO_4$; a 30:40:30 nitrate-Al-perchlorate composition eventually prevailed.

Today, the trend is toward including only finely divided metal and a high explosive central burster in the photoflash flare case, largely to increase safety. Mixing and loading of previous photoflash compositions were notorious for accidents fatal to munitions workers. Moreover, in the field, if a projectile, even from small arms, pierced a photoflash case containing an oxidizer-metal mix, it caused an immediate high-order explosion that invariably destroyed the aircraft and killed the crew. A case with only metal powder and a high explosive burster is less sensitive during loading and handling, and, if damaged during flight, is unlikely to explode before it can be jettisoned or the plane can be evacuated.

Cackett[2] has given the characteristics of photoflash compositions. Figure 1 shows the relation between the flare light output and the action of the camera shutter. Table I lists the output of mixes containing Mg powder and a variety of oxidants.

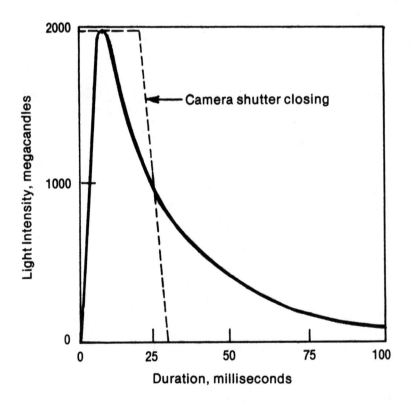

Figure 1. *Output light pulse of photoflash flare[2].*

Table I. Photoflash operating characteristics:
4.5-inch bombs filled with 9 lb of 50:50 Mg-powder mixes

Oxidant	Peak Intensity Megacandles	Total Light Flux Megacandle-seconds	Specific Light Flux (Luminous Efficiency) Candle-seconds/g
$NaNO_3$	223	6.0	3000
KNO_3	243	8.8	4400
$Ba(NO_3)_2$	224	11.6	5800
$Sr(NO_3)_2$	223	11.8	5900
$KClO_4$	415	14.0	6800

Extended burning times

Military actions in Korea and Vietnam demanded longer illumination periods for air-evacuation missions and to protect against night raids. Packages developed for this requirement varied in appearance but contained the same $NaNO_3$-Mg-binder composition and burned with a yellow-white light. Based on the reaction:

$$9Mg + 2NaNO_3 + O_2 \rightarrow 6MgO + Mg_3N_2 + NaO_2$$

the stoichiometric ratio of Mg to $NaNO_3$ was 56:44. The luminosity of this composition exceeded that of all others because of the added contribution of the Na vapor.

Various binders have been used, including those shown in Table II and others such as epoxy resins, acaroid, bakelite, and thiokol rubber.

Table II. Some standard long-burning flares

Country	Composition	Specific Intensity candles/in²
Great Britain	Mg (50%)-$NaNO_3$ (46%)- lithographic varnish (4%)	112,000
USSR	Mg (45%)-$NaNO_3$ (48%)- iditol, shellac (7%)	120,000
USA	Mg (50%)-$NaNO_3$ (43%)- laminac polyester (7%)	110,000

Analysis of the behavior of the Mg-$NaNO_3$ mix, similar to that applied to the B-$BaCrO_4$ delay mix in Chapter 5, showed that the maximum burning rate and the Q inflection point coincided at 50% Mg. Since the burning rate fell when more Mg was added (which increased the thermal conductivity), the conclusion follows that burning propagates by some mechanism other than thermal conduction. Probably heat radiates from one zone to the next. Data from Gilbert[3] in Figure 2 leads to the same conclusion. Thus, the burning rate should not be controlled by varying the Mg content but by varying the additives.

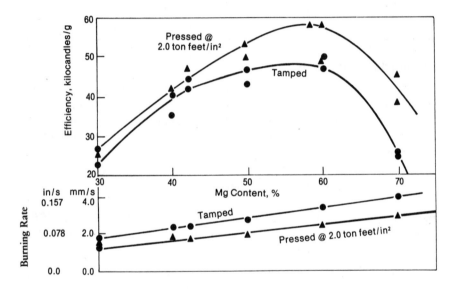

Figure 2. *Variation of* Mg-NaNO$_3$ *flare performance with* Mg *content*[3].

In practice, the control has usually been the amount or type of binder, but the British have also obtained excellent results with CaC$_2$O$_4$, and apparently even superior results with oxamide. CaC$_2$O$_4$ additions should not exceed 12% for best performance, and 3% additions actually increase the luminous efficiency.

High-temperature reaction reversal

The Mg-NaNO$_3$ reaction is reversible and one of a class of considerable interest in pyrotechnics. Another member of this class was discussed in Chapter VI:

$$Zn + CO \rightarrow ZnO + C \quad \text{at room temperature}$$
$$ZnO + C \rightarrow Zn + CO \quad \text{at high temperature (Zn smelting)}$$

The reversal temperature, T_{rev}, is that at which the enthalpy and entropy terms in the thermodynamic equation equal each other: $\Delta H = T\Delta S$[4]. The enthalpy term is calculated from the difference between the heats of formation of the reaction products, including the heat of sublimation of Zn which is a gas at the reversal temperature ($1260\,°K$ or $987\,°C$), and those of the reactants. Similarly, the entropy change is the difference between the total entropy of the products and that of the reactants, again considering Zn as a gas. Such a calculation is only an approximation because the assumed enthalpy and entropy values differ from those prevailing at higher temperatures, but it agrees well enough with experiment and with more refined calculations.

Since CO has been detected in the combustion products of the Mg-NaNO$_3$-laminac illuminating flare[5], MgO must react with C much as does ZnO:

$$MgO + C \rightarrow CO + Mg \text{ (gas)}$$

Heats of formation and entropies are:

	Heat of formation kcal/g mol	Entropy cal/mol °K
MgO	-143.8	6.4
C	0.0	4.0
CO	-26.4	47.0
Mg (gas)	35.9	35.5

Therefore, $\Delta H = 35.9 - 26.4 + 143.8 = 153.3$ kcal/g mol, and $\Delta S = 35.5 + 47.0 - 4.0 - 6.4 = 72.1$ cal/mol °K. Equating $\Delta H = T\Delta S$ gives $T_{rev} = 153,300/72.1 = 2130\,°K$ or $1860\,°C$.

For another pyrotechnic reaction:

$$Al_2O_3 + 3C \rightarrow 3CO + 2Al$$

the calculated T_{rev} is $2140\,°C$.

Dannatt and Ellingham[6] determined these temperatures more precisely, plotting the free energy, $\Delta G°$, versus temperature for various reactions, some of which are shown in Figure 3. Reversal temperatures can be read from the intersections between the CO formation line and those of the metal oxides. Mellor[7] also measured the reversal temperatures experimentally. Table III compares the values from the three sources.

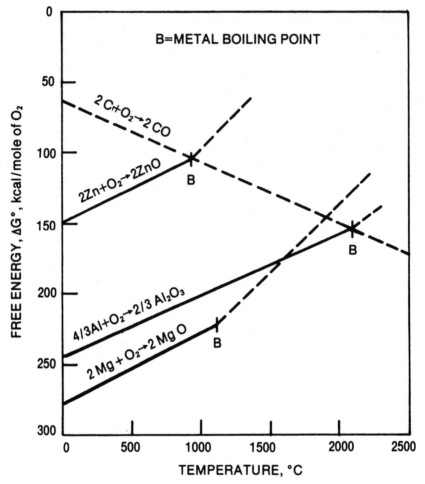

Figure 3. *Free energy vs temperature for various oxide reactions*[6].

Table III. Calculated vs experimental reaction reversal temperatures

	Calculated		Experimental
Reaction	Dannatt and Ellingham	McLain	Mellor
	°C	°C	°C
ZnO + C → CO + Zn	960	987	1025
MgO + C → CO + Mg	1850	1860	1950
Al₂O₃ + 3C → 3CO + Al	2100	2140	

Reversal temperatures are significant in flare technology since they represent an inhibiting mechanism. For example, when the Mg-$NaNO_3$ system rises to the reversal temperature, 1860 °C, the onset of an endothermic reaction limits both the rate of burning and the attained temperature. Measured temperatures have characteristically been lower than calculated values for this reaction. Lower temperatures mean lower radiation intensity (for a black body the total radiated energy would vary as the fourth power of the absolute temperature). This strongly points to the advisability of using a non-carbonaceous binder.

Another point of interest is the intersection of the Al_2O_3 and MgO lines on the Dannatt and Ellingham graph at about 1650 °C. Since this is well below most pyrotechnic burning temperatures, it suggests that Al could be used to reduce MgO in an appropriate system.

SIGNALLING

The essential difference between illuminating and signalling flares is the addition of color to the signal flame. Both types need high intensity, but candlepower is secondary to color quality in signal compositions.

Colored flames originated fairly recently, largely through the discovery and preparation of $KClO_3$ by C.L. Berthollet in the late 18th century. Before this low-temperature oxidizer became available, flame color was a vain hope because high burning temperatures bleached the flame to white. Although $KClO_4$ and NH_4ClO_4 are used in compositions today, they serve principally to make mixing, handling, and pressing safer and do not produce the color depth and fidelity obtained with $KClO_3$.

The fireworks industry has known for many years that halogen compounds improve a flame's color quality. This is another reason for the popularity of chlorine compounds such as the chlorates and perchlorates, hexachlorbenzene, Hg_2Cl_2 (calomel), and, more recently, polyvinyl chloride, in signal flares. The contribution of chlorine to flame color may very well have started when a past pyrotechnician made an analogy between a flare's spectral quality and the colors produced by the well-known Beilstein copper-wire test for the presence of halogens in organic molecules.

History

The first signal flares seem to have been hand-held Bengal Lights, reputedly composed of KNO_3, S, and As_2S_3 (orpiment), which had a pale blue-white color. Another historically famous flare, still in use, is the *Very* light, invented by a U.S. naval officer, Edward W. Very (1874—1910). It is white or colored and is fired from a special pistol. Variations of the Very light and also fired from a special handgun are the aircraft recognition signals, usually consisting of three stars with Al-foil-wrapped compositions in various color combinations and sequences.

A unique World War II product of the pyrotechnic art was the German *Pfeifpatrone*. Equipped with a parachute and launched from a handgun, it captured attention by means of a loud whistle, a colored smoke, and an intense but brief blue-white light. Another World War II flare was the *Day-Nite* rescue signal made for the U.S. armed forces. It was a metal can which emitted a bright red flame from one end and an orange smoke cloud from the other. They are still being made and are recommended for use by small craft owners.

Fusees

Railway and highway fusees are other flares in common use today. They are made in varying lengths of convolute-wound Kraft paper and usually equipped for scratcher-matchhead ignition. Typical compositions are given in Table IV.

Table IV. Typical fusee compositions

Matchhead		Scratcher		Red-fire Mix	
	%		%		%
Liquid shellac	40	Lacquer	61	Sr(NO$_3$)$_2$	71.0
Sr(NO$_3$)$_2$	3	Pumice	2.2	S	10.7
Quartz	6	Red phosphorus	26	KClO$_4$	7.6
Charcoal	2	Butyl acetate	10.8	Sawdust, wood flour 1:1	5.2
KClO$_4$	14			Paraffin oil	1.6
KClO$_3$	28			Fuel Oil	1.4
Wood flour	5			Corn starch	1.8
Marble dust	2.0			Stearic acid (varied to adjust burning rate)	0.75

An older and simpler fusee mix contains 65% KClO$_3$, 9% burnt umber, 13% SrCO$_3$, and 13% fine charcoal. Other compositions may be found in Davis[8] and Weingart[9]. The latest improvement in fusee mixes is the use of polyvinyl chloride as binder and color enhancer. When added to a modified KClO$_3$-burnt umber-SrCO$_3$-charcoal mix, it reduces by almost one third the quantity of mix required to give the same color quality, candlepower, and burning time.

Military Signals

Military signal flares differ from others primarily in the use of powdered Mg metal to increase the candlepower. Some representative compositions from Ellern[10] are shown in Table V.

Table V. Representative military signal flare compositions

	Red	Green	Yellow
	%	%	%
Magnesium	29	15	26
Gilsonite	2	2	2
Oil	2	2	2
Cupric oxide	-	2	-
$Ba(NO_3)_2$	-	45	29
$Sr(NO_3)_2$	34	16	-
$KClO_4$	29	-	23
Sodium oxalate	-	-	13

Other compositions are presented in Shidlovskiy[1], Cackett[2], and Lancaster et al[11].

The higher intensity of military signal flares is accompanied by a higher burning temperature and bleaching of color, especially with blue and green flares. Green flares derive their color from the $BaCl_2$ emission band. As the temperature rises, the BaO^+ emission band increasingly contributes colors in the orange-to-red portion of the spectrum. In attempts to moderate the burning temperature, some green-flare compositions are now made with $Ba(ClO_3)_2$ ·H_2O as an oxidizer. Another contains Cu filings as an additional source of blue-green emission.

Blue is the most difficult color to achieve and bleaches severely when intensity is raised. The blue color comes from the $CuCl^+$ emission band. The most beautiful blues are made with $KClO_3$ (this technology is discussed in Chapter XI, *Fireworks*). $KClO_4$ is also used and NH_4ClO_4 has begun to appear in some compositions, but neither of these produces as good a blue as does $KClO_3$ because of their higher flame temperatures.

Tracers. Tracer ammunition is yet another military flare application. It involves unique problems associated with the rotational speed and wake of the projectile and the tremendous acceleration imparted by the propellant. For small arms, the spin rate is typically 400,000 rpm and the acceleration 200,000 g (6,440,000 ft/sec²). Combustion residues must be slag-like because low-pressure regions in the wake would suck out gaseous reaction products and cause propagation failure. Considering the limited volume allotted to the tracer composition and the high visibility desired at long ranges, the pyrotechnic problem is formidable. A fairly recent requirement is a dark ignition period to prevent exposure of the gun's position and to protect the firer from being blinded by the glare at night. Special first-fire compositions were designed to meet this requirement. Table VI lists six representative tracer compositions.

Table VI. Representative tracer compositions

Material	1	2	3	4	5	6
	%	%	%	%	%	%
Mg	32	28	28	7.5	15	30
SrO_2	32					5
SrC_2O_4	22.5	8				
Hg_2Cl_2	7.5					
Starch	4.0					
Acaroid resin	2.0					
$Sr(NO_3)_2$		40	55	55		52
$KClO_4$		20				
Calcium resinate	4					
Polyvinyl chloride			17	7		
BaO_2					84	
Zinc stearate					1	
Zirconium hydride				30.5		
Boiled linseed oil						10
Talc						3

Pulsating signals. Red pulsating flares are a recent development in military signals demonstrated by F.-W. Wasmann[12,13] of the Institute for Chemistry of Propellants and Explosives at meetings in Karlsruhe, West Germany and Guildford, England in 1975. Unlike conventional systems, pulsating flares do not burn at either a constant or continuously progressive rate, but fluctuate cyclically. Pulse frequencies can be varied from about 0.1 to 1000 Hz with changes in composition, making them feasible for use in code sequences. Uwe Krone[14] cited possible pulsed distress flares and parachute pulsed-signal cartridges at the Karlsruhe meeting. Two representative pulsating-signal compositions and frequencies are:

Material	% for 100 Hz	% for 0.2 Hz
Strontium perchlorate tetrahydrate	50	50
Methacrylic acid-methyl ester	10	25
Pentaerythritol dinitrate-diacrylate	40	25

Infrared (IR) decoy flares. The advent of heat-seeking missiles brought about the development of the IR decoy flare as a countermeasure. This flare is designed to duplicate approximately the infrared emissions to which the missiles are sensitive, thus deflecting the missile toward the decoy and away from the aircraft. One possible IR decoy flare composition is:

Mg (No. 15 granulation)	11 parts
Powdered teflon	6 parts
Kel-F wax	3 parts

I light my candle from their torches.
Robert Burton

Chapter VII

REFERENCES

1. Shidlovskiy, A.A., *Foundations of Pyrotechnics,* Report FTD-II-63-758 (trans. DDC AD 602 687), Air Force Systems Command, Wright-Patterson AFB, Ohio, 1964.

2. Cackett, J.C., *Monograph on Pyrotechnic Compositions,* Royal Armament Research and Development Establishment, Fort Halstead, Seven Oaks, Kent, England, 1965 (RESTRICTED).

3. Gilbert, J.D., *Burning Rate Modification in Resin Bonded Flares,* in Pyrochem International, University of Surrey, 1975; sponsored by the Royal Armament Research and Development Establishment, Langhurst, Horsham, Sussex, England.

4. Mclain, J.H., in *Proceedings of the 6th International Symposium on the Reactivity of Solids* 1968, Wiley-Interscience, New York, 1969.

5. Douda, B.F., RDTR No. 131 in *Proceedings of the 1st Pyrotechnics Seminar,* U.S. Naval Ammunition Depot, Crane, Ind., October 1968.

6. Dannatt, C.W. and Ellingham,H.J.T., *The Physical Chemistry of Process Metallurgy,* Discussions of the Faraday Society, No. 4 (1948), p. 130.

7. Mellor, J.W., *A Comprehensive Treatise on Inorganic and Theoretical Chemistry,* Longmans, Green, London.

8. Davis., T.L., in *Engineering Design Handbook,* "Explosive Trains," AMCP 706-179, U.S. Army Materiel Command, March 1965.

9. Weingart, G.W., *Pyrotechnics,* 2nd ed., Chemical Publishing Co., New York, 1947.

10. Ellern, H., *Military and Civilian Pyrotechnics,* Chemical Publishing Co., New York, 1968; p. 361.

11. Lancaster, R., Shimizu, T., Butler, R.E.A., and Hall, R.G., *Fireworks Principles and Practice,* Chemical Publishing Co., New York, 1972.

12. Wasmann, F.-W., "Pyrotechnics, Basic Principles, Technology and Applications," in *Jahrestagung,* Institut fur Chemie der Treib- und Explosivstoffe, 1965, pp. 239-250.

13. Wasmann, F.-W., "Pulsating Pyrotechnic Systems," *op. cit.* reference 3.

14. Krone, U., "Strahlungsemission in intervallenoscillierende verbrennung Pyrotechnischer satze," *op. cit.* reference 12.

Chapter VIII

HEAT

Fire is the best of servants, but what a master!
T. Carlyle

A spontaneous solid-solid reaction always produces heat so that heat normally accompanies the pyrotechnic generation of smoke, light, color, motion, and noise. Although the pyrotechnician often considers heat only a by-product, at best a necessary evil, in some pyrotechnic applications heat or flame is the desired product. It may be used for either constructive or destructive purposes.

CONSTRUCTIVE APPLICATIONS OF PYROTECHNIC HEAT

M1 fire starters

When mountain warfare troops requested igniters that could make a fire from wet or frozen wood, first efforts were directed toward adapting the Kraus-Evers mix, a castable (while hot) combination of $KClO_4$, charcoal, and paraffin wax. After an exhaustive study of the effect of varying the three ingredients, experimenters achieved very high flame temperatures, but candles made from the mixtures were dismal failures as fire starters. Abundant deposits of KCl fireproofed the surface of the wood.

A different and successful development resulted in the M1 Fire Starter detailed in Figure 1. Hundreds of thousands of these devices have provided some comfort for many men and women under deplorable conditions.

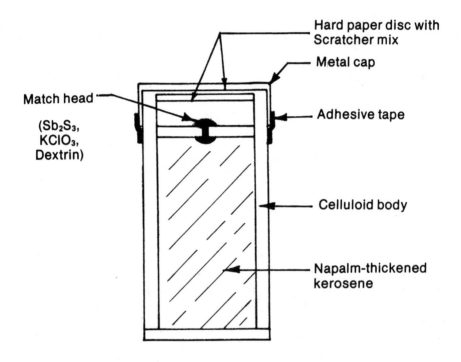

Figure 1. M1 *fire starter.*

Self-heating food cans

A World War II British development invented by Caldwell and Gillies, the self-heating food can also provided comfort to troops in the field. It is pictured in Figure 2, as described by Taylor[1], who states that several million cans were used by British and American armed forces, especially Commando troops.

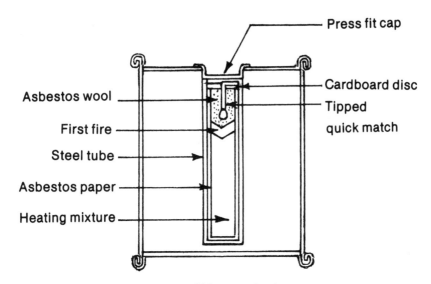

Figure 2. *Self-heating food can*[1].

Compositions used in the self-heating food can were:

First fire		Heating	
Pb_3O_4	64%	Fe_3O_4	50%
$CaSi_2$	27%	$CaSi_2$	50%
China clay	9%		

Another ingenious device for food warming, patented by O.G. Bennett[3], contained the following pyrotechnic heat mix:

Zn dust	33.8%	
$BaCrO_4$	43.4%	
MnO_2	22.8%	(calcined for 2 hr over 400 °C)

Pyronol torch

A relatively recent development is the Pyronol torch used by salvage crews at sea to cut through cables and steel structures. According to a 1970 report, the torch could cut through 4 inches of stainless steel in 0.025 seconds at a depth of 2000 feet. The torch's cutting agent is presumed to be gaseous iron at a very high temperature.

Early in 1971, a detailed study[4] of the torch was undertaken to analyze its chemistry and improve its performance. The report concluded that the overall reaction is:

$$2Al + Ni + Fe_2O_3 \longrightarrow Al_2O_3 + NiO + 2Fe$$

with a heat output of 0.91 kcal/g. Although the empirically determined composition worked well, it differed from stoichiometric proportions:

	Stoichiometric, %	Empirical, %
Fe_2O_3	54.4	34.3
Al	18.6	27.4
Ni	20.0	31.3
$(C_2F_4)_n$ binder, fluid	7.0	7.0

The investigators concluded that an alloying reaction, $Ni + 2Al \longrightarrow Al_2Ni$, must be serving a dual role as preheater to the oxidation reaction and liquid medium to increase the burning rate and heat output. If so, then increasing the amount of Ni and Al (maintaining the stoichiometric ratio 20.0: 18.6), while keeping the amount of Fe_2O_3 constant, should increase the contribution of the alloying reaction. If this contribution is doubled, compared with the stoichiometric condition, the composition becomes:

	%
Fe_2O_3	37.2
Al	27.4
Ni	28.4
$(C_2F_4)_n$	7.0

which is close to the empirical formulation and tends to confirm the hypothetical role of the Ni-Al reaction.

Doping the Fe_2O_3 with CuO gave the torch more heat and better performance. Extending this principle to work with copper ferrite yielded excellent results. The ferrite was made by decomposing a mixed crystal of $CuSO_4$ $\cdot 5H_2O$ and $FeSO_4 \cdot 7H_2O$ in a 1:2 (U.S. Patent 3,887,479). The calorimetrically measured heat of reaction for a 50:50 mix of $CuFe_2O_4$ and Ti was 1.365 kcal/g whereas for Fe_2O_3 and Ti it was only 0.879 kcal/g.

Helms and Rozner[5] have recently reported using Fe_3O_4 and Cr_2O_3 in addition to Fe_2O_3, and a 50:50 ratio of Al-Mg and Al-Zr. They also cite the use of B, Be, and Bi.

Thermal battery

O.G. Bennett of the Catalyst Research Corporation conceived and reduced to practice an electric battery with indefinitely long shelf life. His basic idea was to use a solid electrolyte which remained inactive until melted by a pyrotechnic mix ignited by a trigger action. Although a variety of such battery designs now exist, they are generally based on a KCl-LiCl eutectic mixture and Z2-impregnated asbestos paper (Z2 is a mixture of Zr and $BaCrO_4$ with or without $KClO_4$). The powdered heating mix is combined with the fibrous material in a water suspension to make "heat paper" designed to produce a predetermined number of calories per square inch. T-2 is an alternative heating mix composed of Zr, Ni, $BaCrO_4$, and $KClO_4$. Although these batteries can be used only once, their reliability and capability of remote initiation have earned them a prominent position in pyrotechnic applications.

Heat block

Another heating device used by the military is the Heat Block. A heat-block composition that delivers $210-230$ cal/g contains:

	%
Fe	47
Sn	6.7
$KClO_4$	8.2
Zr-Ni 30/70	6.3
$BaCrO_4$	13.5
Naphthalene	11.5
Ni	4.8
Carbowax	1.9

Thermite

The previously mentioned Goldschmidt[6] or thermite process produces molten iron by a reaction of Al and hammerscale:

$$8Al + 3Fe_3O_4 \rightarrow 4Al_2O_3 + 9Fe$$

It is used for repairing castings, butt welding, and general railway repairs and has also been applied to the preparation of relatively pure metals or alloys from their oxides:

$$MnO + MnO_2 + 2Al \rightarrow Al_2O_3 + 2\,Mn$$
$$Cr_2O_3 + 2Al \rightarrow Al_2O_3 + Cr$$
$$3Fe_3O_4 + 9TiO_2 + 20Al \rightarrow 9FeTi + 10Al_2O_3$$

If an Fe-Mn (90:10) alloy is required, 9 parts of Fe_3O_4-Al mix can be combined with 1 part of Mn_3O_4-Al mix.

Thermite-type compositions are also packaged in pyrotechnic welding cartridges. Shidlovskiy[7] describes a pyrocartridge containing a magnesium thermite for welding telephone and telegraph wires, and also reports a modified thermite (Fe_3O_4-Al-Mg-FeMn alloy) used to weld grounding wires to metallic structures.

Heating wrap

The Nitro-Nobel company in Sweden has perfected a pyrotechnic heating wrap for curing plastic-cemented joints in large air ducts.

DESTRUCTIVE APPLICATIONS OF PYROTECHNIC HEAT

Gasoline gels

IM gels. Development work started early in 1942 on gelled gasolines to fill incendiary bombs. Very successful gels were made with 8% natural rubber. However, natural rubber was in short supply and considered more necessary for other applications, so a substitute was sought.

The problem was to make the gel cohesive enough to withstand the high stress of the igniter-burster (50:50 Mg-black powder) explosion. The gel had to be dilatant, not thixotropic; it should stiffen under stress and lengthen the burning time rather than expend all its incendiary capacity instantly in one fireball on impact and ignition. Sodium stearate-alcohol solutions and various other fuels and gelling agents were tried without much success.

With the hope that additional branching of the lyophilic "tails" would increase the gel's mechanical strength, investigators tested aluminum naphthenate in gasoline. The resulting gel had outstanding properties but underwent syneresis (bleeding, or separation of the liquid from the gel) at low temperatures.

The next effort, directed toward increasing the lyophilic chain length, was more fruitful. Partially esterified polyisobutyl methacrylate was dissolved in gasoline and then ground $Ca(OH)_2$ was stirred into the solution. After a delay that varied with $Ca(OH)_2$ grain size, the mixture gelled into the desired tacky and tenacious material. In fact, the material, which became standardized as IM gel, was superior to the natural rubber product in both incendiary performance and adaptability to large-scale production. The story of its development, written by Dr. Leo Finkelstein who was in charge of the laboratory, can be found in the World War II Annals of the Chemical Warfare Service.

PT (Pyrotechnic) gels. Attempts were made to improve the incendiary capability of thickened gasoline by adding a pyrotechnic mixture of Mg powder and an oxidizer. The composition designated PTV consists of IM gel and added Mg and $NaNO_3$. Composition PT1 uses a similar pyrotechnic filler. The pyrotechnic gels had a greater calorific output than the non-pyrotechnic types but were not superior incendiaries, partly because the inorganic products of the $Mg-NaNO_3$ reaction formed an insulating crust.

Napalm gel. Napalm, an invention of Professor Louis F. Fieser[8], has become one of the most widely known fuel thickeners to come out of World War II because of its later use in Vietnam. It is a compound soap of aluminum naphthenate and aluminum palmitate from which it derives its name. Although napalm is not itself incendiary, the name is often applied to the incendiary gel formed with kerosene or gasoline, and even to the complete bomb.

Contrary to many published reports, napalm is not even a good thickener for incendiary bomb fuels because gels made with it exhibit syneresis at temperatures near $-40\,°C$ and create a fast-burning inefficient fireball when ignited. In the M69 bomb, a cambric sock enclosing the napalm-gasoline gel reduced the bleeding problem.

The thixotropic properties of napalm gel that detract from its effectiveness in bombs add to its effectiveness in flame-thrower fuel. The requirement is that the fuel stream be quite liquid as it emerges from the nozzle and then rethicken and cohere to allow controlled aiming. (What could be called the first flame thrower was made by a Roman architect named Callinicus who lived from 648 to 685. He prepared a "wet fire which was thrown out from siphons."[9]). Thixotropy of the gel also made possible the practice of low-level dropping of wing-mounted aerial incendiaries. When used for skip bombing into caves, the incendiaries were equipped with modified M15 grenades with white phosphorus igniters. Na-filled grenade igniters were used for bombing water targets.

Thermate

The incendiary bomb that wreaked havoc on the city of Coventry, England, was a hexagonal Mg alloy casting with Al vanes on its tail and a thermate filling similar to that in the AN-M52Al. Thermate used in World War II was a mixture of:

	%
Granular Al	15
Grained Al (atomized)	10
Fe_3O_4	45
$Ba(NO_3)_2$	26
Sulfur	2
Castor oil	2

Ellern[10] cites a later thermate composition containing:

	%
Granular Al	19
Grained Al	3
Fe_3O_4	51
$Ba(NO_3)_2$	22
Laminac	5

Another incendiary bomb loaded with pressed thermate was the AN-M50A2 (now called the M125), larger and heavier than the AN-M52Al (4 vs 2 lb). Its magnesium housing also had an iron nose to aid penetration of tile or slate roofs. The AN-M50A2 was the bomb dropped on Dresden and Hamburg with such telling effect.

An interesting facet of magnesium bomb development was the selection of a suitable first fire. Thermate is difficult to ignite reliably under the best of circumstances. The effect of impact against hard targets makes ignition even more problematic.

The first ignition mixture used was the *British igniter* consisting of:

	%
Si	40
KNO_3	40
Sulfurless meal powder	20

This had many shortcomings and was modified by the addition of 1 part of a 22:13 mix of fine Fe_3O_4 and grained Al to 2 parts of the regular mix. Burning now produced an advantageous slag or molten Fe. However, even the modified mix was too gassy and was replaced by a more satisfactory first fire:

	%
$BaCrO_4$	70
Mg	30

After the war, a surveillance testing program revealed that the $BaCrO_4$ was oxidizing the Mg even during storage so that only two thirds of the original metal was left after four years. Another mix was developed, containing 50% pigment-grade Fe_2O_3 and 50% Ti, which was stable during long-term high-temperature storage.

Safe destroyers

Safe destroyers were developed to quickly and completely destroy the contents of a safe to prevent documents from falling into enemy hands. The destroyer was a large, rectangular, galvanized-steel container loaded with thermite and a sodium silicate binder and attached to the ceiling of the safe. When actuated, the mix produced a great deal of heat and a large quantity of molten iron. Ignition originated in a 50:50 Fe_2O_3-Ti first-fire mix at three sources, two gasless electric squibs, and a manually-set short-handled M201A1 fuze.

Pouch destroyers. A similar requirement arises to destroy documents in a pouch carried by a courier in danger of being captured. However, the task of burning such papers proved to be more difficult than expected. In the first tests, thermite merely charred tightly packed paper and produced some holes, but left about 80% of the pouches' contents easily legible. This result was related to the fact (not generally realized outside the paper industry) that much of the paper consisted of non-cellulosic material (e.g., one of the major uses of TiO_2 is as a filler in paper). The problem was solved by using a special paper impregnated with an oxidant ($NaNO_3$ or KNO_3), developed and specified with the cooperation of the paper industry. The pouch-destroyer igniter was a 47:47:6 mix of $NaNO_3$, sucrose, and charcoal.

AN-M14 grenade

This thermite-filled grenade is classified as an incendiary munition but its principal use is to eat through or weld together metal shells or structures. An acceptance test requires penetration through 1 inch of boiler plate in less than 30 seconds. An M14 grenade set off in the breech or muzzle of a field gun renders it both inoperable and unsalvageable. Oil storage tanks are another prime target.

HEI loads

High explosive incendiary (HEI) compositions were standard loading materials for 20-mm and 40-mm rounds during World War II. The explosive mix was a compound of high explosive and pyrotechnic materials, formed as cylindrical pellets and then inserted and consolidated in a cylindrical casing. The incendiary component, sometimes consisting only of metal such as mischmetal, Al, Mg, or Zr, was usually shaped into a hollow cylinder with an inside diameter dimensioned to accommodate the solid high-explosive charge. As the high-explosive character of the round might lead one to expect, the incendiary effects are very short-lived, effective mainly as igniters of fuel tanks.

Shidlovskiy[11] cites a 50:50 Mg-KClO$_4$ mix used in small-caliber projectiles to ignite liquid fuels. He also describes the composition in the German 20-mm shells as 76% Hexogen (Cyclonite, RDX), 20% Al, and 4% phlegmatizer (probably a high molecular weight wax which also served as a binder).

Fusible links

Fusible links are similar to the fusible metal used in water sprinkler systems for fire safety. They hold parts of an assembly together until the links are melted by pyrotechnically generated heat. Fusible links have now largely been supplanted by frangible bolts and other explosively severed devices.

And by night in a pillar of fire
Exodus 13:21

Chapter VIII

REFERENCES

1. Taylor, J., *Solid Propellant and Exothermic Compositions,* George Newnes, London, 1959.
2. Caldwell, W.A. and Gillies, J., *Ind. Chemist* **26,** 301 (1950).
3. Bennett, O.G., U.S. Patents 2,500,790 and 2,531,548 (1950).
4. McLain, J.H. and Hoopes, M.T., *The Chemistry of the Pyronol Torch,* Contract No. N00174-71-C-0013, NAVEODFAC, Indian Head, Md., 1971.
5. Helms, H.H. and Rozner, A., U.S. Patent 3,695,951 (1972).
6. Goldschmidt, H., German Patent 96,317 (1895).
7. Shidlovskiy, A.A., *Foundations of Pyrotechnics,* Report FTD-II-63-758 (trans. DDC AD 602 687), Air Force Systems Command, Wright-Patterson AFB, Ohio, 1964; pp. 379,380.
8. Feiser. L.F., U.S. Patent 2,606,107 (1952).
9. Van Gelder, A.P. and Schlatter, H., *History of the Explosives Industry in America,* Columbia University Press, New York, 1927, p. 7.
10. Ellern, H., *Military and Civilian Pyrotechnics,* Chemical Publishing Co., New York, 1968.
11. Shidlovskiy, A.A., *op. cit.;* pp. 306,307.

Chapter IX

MOTION

Archimedes had stated, that given the force, any given weight might be moved . . . .

Plutarch

The object of pyrotechnic burning is often motion, ranging from the generalized expansion of an unshaped explosion to the channeled thrust against a projectile. Although the action may be accompanied by other pyrotechnic effects such as heat, light, sound, noise, and esthetic excitement, these are then secondary to the desire to make something move.

BLACK POWDER

The oldest and most significant of all pyrotechnic mixes that produce motion is black powder. It was the first propellant as well as the first blasting agent. Tenney L. Davis[1] rates its discovery as "one of the most important of all time," a statement with which most people concur. As the first chemical earth mover, it allowed man to excavate, to construct, and to mine minerals. Since a basic factor in the material development of mankind is command and control of energy, black powder, along with the lever and the wheel, has made a major contribution.

History

The origin of black powder is shrouded in controversy. Among the claimants are the Chinese, Indians, Greeks, Arabs, Germans, and English. However, it is practically certain that black powder was not known before the Crusades (1097-1291) since its principal ingredient, saltpeter (KNO_3), was mentioned only in China where it was used in fireworks in the tenth century[2].

Some points of interest in the development and application of black powder are known:

> 1214-1294 - Roger Bacon gave explicit directions for purifying saltpeter and described a mixture of 7 parts (42%) saltpeter, 5 parts (29%) charcoal, and 5 parts sulfur, but did not mention its use as a propellant.
> 1193-1280 - Albertus Magnus, Count Albert of Bollstadt, mentioned a powder prepared of saltpeter, carbon, and sulfur which creates thunder and causes rockets to rise.
> 1313 - Berthold Schwarz (the Powder Monk) invented firearms.
> 1435 - The first stamp mill began operating in Nuremburg.
> 1627 - Black powder was first used for mining in Hungary.
> 1632-1645 - Mining with black powder spread to Freiberg.
> 1648 - Mining with black powder began in Falun, Sweden.
> 1669 - Black powder was used for road and tunnel excavating in Switzerland.

Black powder had three major periods of evolution. From 1313 to 1450, it was fine grained and varied widely in composition. From 1450 to 1700, both composition and grain size changed when large-grained powder was found to be more effective in cannon. From 1700-1800, only grain size changed because the 75:15:10 KNO_3-C-S composition had become universally accepted and performance depended largely on when and how the powder was compounded.

It is hard to conceive of a pyrotechnic mix that has had a more pronounced effect on history. In warfare alone, the quality of black powder was often decisive. Napoleon was the first general who had enough confidence in his field artillery to fire over the heads of his advancing infantry. In naval battles, the reproducibility of the powder was all important in determining whether well-aimed cannon balls hit the target. If the powder burned too fast or too slowly, the projectiles flew too high or fell short into the sea. High-quality powder was absolutely necessary for the long-barrel rifles that played such a vital role in the American revolution.

Manufacture

The present method of black-powder manufacture consists of the following steps:

1. Sulfur and charcoal are ground together in a ball mill.
2. KNO_3 is ground separately.
3. The ground powders are mixed by tumbling them together.

4. The mix is consolidated while wet in a wheel mill (stamp mills were outlawed in Europe in 1772). Figure 1 is a diagram of a modern wheel mill. Its iron wheels are typically about 6 ft in diameter with 20-inch wide faces (milling surfaces), weigh 10 to 12 tons, and are mounted free on a horizontal shaft over a 9-ft diameter iron bed.

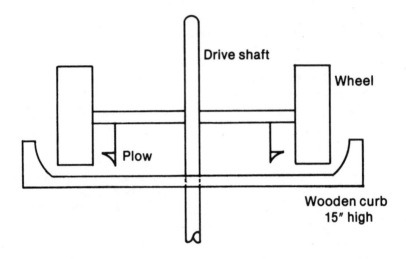

Figure 1. *Wheel mill for wet consolidation of black powder.*

Each charge for a mill this size weighs 300 lb and is milled for 4 to 5 hours. The moisture content after milling is 2½%.

5. The mill cake is broken up by wooden rollers.

6. The powder is pressed into 1-inch thick, 24-inch square cakes with a density of 1.74 to 1.80 g/cm³.

7. The pressed cake is broken up by coarse-toothed cutting rollers.

8. The broken cake is taken to the corning mill which consists of sets of rollers that crack the cake to size and separate various grain sizes.

9. The material is reeled (fines are sifted out).

10. The powder is glazed by tumbling.

Substitutes for black powder have been sought for many years with variable success. Although some compositions have been developed that perform well in certain traditional black-powder applications, a universally satisfactory substitute has not yet been found. For example, smokeless powder has replaced black powder as a propellant in some rockets and in rifles and other guns, but black powder is still much used as a primer in large-caliber navy ammunition, as an ejection charge in military applications, and as a lifting charge in all sorts of fireworks.

Black-powder manufacture in the United States has dwindled to one source, the former du Pont plant in northeastern Pennsylvania now operated by Gearhart-Owens.

Properties

Much of the reason for black powder's longevity lies in its *quickness*, which is a function of the manufacturing process and the chemical reactivity of the powder's constituents. Black powder is a unique material. Davis[1] has commented that " . . . grains of black powder are not porous - the sulfur appears to have colloidal properties and to fill completely the spaces between the small particles of the other components." What Davis meant by *colloidal* is not exactly clear, but if he implied thixotropy (flow or plasticity under pressure), he was certainly correct. It is sulfur's thixotropy that gives black powder its high grain integrity and makes it behave almost as a compound rather than a mixture.

A second reason for the special character of black powder is the properties of KNO_3. The KNO_3 crystal undergoes a sharp solid-solid transition (rhombic to trigonal) at about 130 °C which "loosens" the structure (see Chapter IV) and makes the substance easier to ignite. This transition has been called the *nitrate spin* and the nitrate ion has been likened to a three-legged stool that spins about its vertical axis. It spins easily because the oxygen ions in the nitrate cluster are indistinguishable from each other and readily interchange positions. (By contrast, the chlorate ion does not spin so easily but has a built-in looseness because one leg of its "stool" is shorter than the others, which distorts the structure and opens the ion to chemical attack.)

Finally, the behavior of black powder also derives from the purgative action of charcoal on SO_2 described previously in Chapter IV. Adsorption of SO_2 by the charcoal is an important factor in the combustion of both sulfur and charcoal and helps the sulfur to perform its function as tinder.

Thus, black powder is not just a random mix of pulverized substances but a consolidated chemical entity with very special properties.

Pyrodex

No discussion of black powder would be complete without mention of Pyrodex, the latest and most successful candidate for a true black-powder substitute. Pyrodex was the result of attempts by Dan Pawlak[3] to develop a lower-cost alternative to black powder especially for firearms hobbyists. Pawlak believed he could formulate a propellant that would duplicate the black-powder pressure-temperature characteristic in firearms as shown in Figure 2.

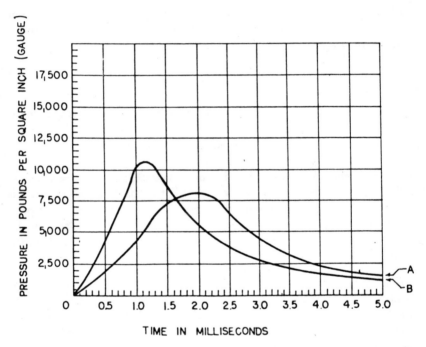

Figure 2. *Pyrodex vs black-powder pressure-time characteristic in firearms.* **A.** *Pyrodex.* **B.** *3FG black powder.*

Pyrodex proved to be a good replacement for black powder in firearms ammunition. It produces the familiar white smoke and even a black-powder smell. However, its range of use in other applications is limited because it is harder to ignite than black powder.

The Pyrodex Corporation manufactured the new material until January 1977 when an explosion destroyed the plant and killed Pawlak and three associates. The plant has now been rebuilt and Pyrodex is again being manufactured at Herington, Kansas and is distributed by the Hodgdon Powder company of Shawnee Mission, Kansas. Classified by the Bureau of Explosives as a flammable solid, Pyrodex can be shipped by most common carriers.

ROCKETS

Rockets have long been used for entertainment or celebration in fireworks and, for more than 100 years, to deliver breeches-buoy lines to ships in distress. However, it is widely, but erroneously, assumed that they were only recently applied to warfare. Actually, the Chinese used black-powder rockets almost 800 years ago to repel a Mongolian cavalry charge. In 1780, Rajah Hyder Ali routed the British army at the battle of Guntur with the use of rockets. Thereafter, Colonel William Congreve (later Sir William) of the British artillery undertook to develop rockets for bombardment. The results of his efforts are recorded in the U.S. national anthem written by Francis Scott Key during the British siege of Fort McHenry in Baltimore harbor in 1812.

It is true that rockets did not come into general military use until World War II, and then they were no longer all powered by black powder. The British developed an effective 3-inch antiaircraft rocket that used a double-base propellant, and an underwater rocket called the *Hedgehog* which supplanted the depth bomb for submarine defense. The U.S. rocket, dubbed the *Bazooka,* was devastating against tanks. However, the rocket the Allies used most was a throwback to the old Congreve bombardment type, fired from ship to shore or from aircraft to surface targets. This was the 4.5-inch rocket first launched on a large scale in the invasion of Sicily. A rapid-fire rocket barrage was so fierce that a 200-foot landing craft could momentarily attain the equivalent firepower of several large battleships.

Black powder still supplies the thrust for many of the smaller descendants of the early rockets. For example, some military rockets still in production are the hand-held types M125A1, M126A1, and M127A1 which contain hollow-cylinder black-powder propulsion pellets inhibited with Pettman cement. Figure 3 shows a cross section of the M126A1 and M127A1. The propellant grain consists of 91% black powder (particles sized so that no more than 3% fail to pass a #20 sieve and no more than 60% fail to pass a #40 sieve) and 9% $CaCO_3$, pressed to a density of 1.82 to 1.89 g/cm^3 and a moisture content of 1.8 to 2.5%. Figure 4 shows the grain shape and size. Grain weight is approximately 13 g.

These devices are used for nighttime signalling and reach an average height of 700 feet. The motor is the same in all three, but the M125A1 produces five

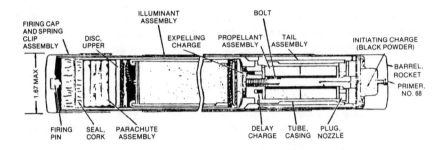

Figure 3 M126A1-M127A1 *hand-held ground illumination signal rocket.*

free-falling white stars, the 126A1 produces a parachute-suspended red star with a nominal burning time of 50 seconds, and the M127A1 produces a white star with a slightly faster burning rate and higher candle power. The rates of descent in relatively still air are 8 ft/sec for the M125A1 and 10 to 15 ft/sec for the M126A1 and M127A1.

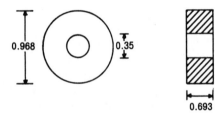

Figure 4. M126A1-M127A1 *propellant grain.*

An educational and interesting nonmilitary application of pyrotechnics to the creation of motion is model rocketry, which is also a modern consumer of black powder. The National Association of Rocketry deserves much credit for promoting this safe and scientific pursuit. Figure 5 shows a typical model-

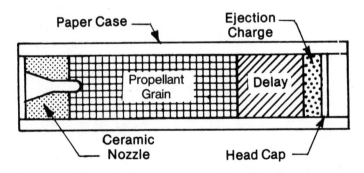

Figure 5. *Cross section of model rocket motor*.

rocket motor[4] available in hobby shops throughout the world. The propellant grain is pressed black powder slowed with wax, talc, or chalk; the ejection charge is granular black powder; and the case is convolute-wound kraft paper.

SMOKE-SHELL EJECTION

Black powder is also used to eject shells containing smoke mixes from small short-barrel mortars on tanks and other military surface vehicles. Because the smooth-bore mortar barrels are very short, allowing little burning time, and the clearance around the projectile is relatively large, requiring rapid gas generation to build up sufficient ejection pressure in spite of high gas leakage, the propellant must be exceptionally "quick."

GAS GENERATORS

Gas generators, in general, can be a source of motion. One of the earliest attempts to produce a gas-pressure ram pyrotechnically instead of with a cumbersome compressed-air tank was the one-shot portable flame thrower. The gas source was a 1-inch diameter, 6-inch long cylinder of Russian solventless powder. The powder grain was inhibited with Tygon tubing and fitted with a gauze pad which supported a 50:50 igniter mixture of black powder and Mg.

Another device based on this principle was a fire extinguisher for a multiple-engine aircraft. Laboratory tests proved that an engine fire could be extinguished in flight if enough of the extinguishing agent could be delivered to the fire soon enough. This could be done with compressed gas, but the weight of the thick-walled tanks required to contain the pressure was prohibitive for aircraft. The use of three grains of cast double-base propellant with double-end burning solved the problem. Gas-generator starting cartridges are also used to power aircraft turbines and naval torpedos and to operate guidance vanes.

Another very successful application of pyrotechnic gas generators is the class of cartridge-actuated devices used for such purposes as pilot-and-seat and stores ejection.

Safety bags

Perhaps the most challenging pyrotechnic problem in the last 20 years is posed by the inflatable safety bag for automobiles. The problem is formidable, but the objective of reducing the number and severity of injuries in automo-

bile accidents is certainly worthy. Some obvious requirements of the safety
bag are:

Ignition and inflation must be extremely quick (1-10 ms).

Gases generated for inflation must be nontoxic and relatively
cool.

Operation should not create an open flame or free incandescent
particles.

The device must be highly reliable: it should not operate acci-
dentally or prematurely and should never fail to operate when called
on.

The reaction should not be susceptible to runaway acceleration
that might burst the bag.

Some less obvious, but possibly equally important, requirements are:

The sensing and trigger mechanism must respond very quickly
and reliably and without false alarms.

The equipment should be easy to replace, long-lived, and relatively
inexpensive.

A number of gas-generating formulations have been suggested for inflating bags and similar applications. One from Takeo Shimizu[5] consists of:

Guanidine nitrate   80 to 98%
MnO_2 20 to 2%

A 90:10 mix yields 90 liters/kg at a gas temperature of 200 °C.

Doin et al[6] describe another formulation:

88 parts 16-micron $KClO_4$
10 parts cellulose acetate binder
5 parts tricresylphosphate plasticizer
0.5 parts carbon black

When formed into a 45-g bundle of 50 strands, 6 mm in diameter by 25 mm
long, and burned in a 45-mm-diameter spherical combustion chamber, the
mix produced gases consisting of 40% O_2, 60% CO_2, and less than 0.04%

CO. Passage through an 8-cm-diameter tube over 90 g of $KClO_3$ pellets (4 mm in diameter by 4 mm long) increased the O_2 to 77% and reduced the CO_2 to 23%. Subsequent passage over 170 g of $NaHCO_3$ coolant pellets, 4 mm in diameter by 4 mm long, produced a final gas composed of 39.5% O_2, 37% CO_2, 23.4% H_2O, less than 0.06% CO, and less than 2 ppm NO_x.

MacSenzie[7] lists two formulas for producing cool gas:

	%	%
NaN_3	58	58
SiO_2	2	2
Viton A	30	30
$Na_2C_2O_4$	10	
$NaHCO_3$		10

McCulloch[8] describes a self-extinguishing nontoxic-gas-generating composition especially suitable for inflating life rafts:

	%
NH_4ClO_4	60
NH_4Cl	20
Polyurethane	19.9
Fe_2O_3	0.1

which has a burning rate of 0.168 in/sec at 1000 psi and 77 °F and is self-extinguishing at pressures greater than 1000 psi. A life raft must have entrained $NaHCO_3$ pellets to absorb the large quantities of HCl produced.

Many other proposed compositions generally contain an alkali metal azide. One of the more novel is a 25:75 mix of nickel formate and $KClO_3$. This seems designed to produce CO and oxidize it to CO_2 and would require a suitable trap for NiO released in the reaction. It would be strange if $KClO_3$, the best and coolest oxidizer, did not play a prominent role in the solution of the gas-generation problem.

ELECTRO-EXPLOSIVE INITIATORS

All the above applications require electrical initiation for which many small initiators, or squibs, have been developed. They supply a spit of flame, a jet of incandescent particles, a rapidly rising pressure pulse, or a shock wave. Probably the first such initiator was the electric blasting cap which lead to the subsequent development of the safety match and the fireworks squib. The space program heightened the need and varied the requirements for such devices.

Flame squib

As its name implies, the flame squib is used solely to ignite pyrotechnic material. Figure 6 shows its size and construction.

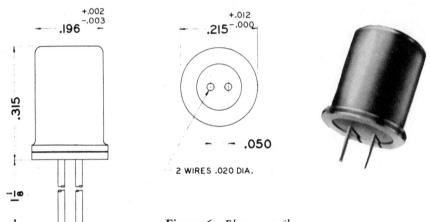

Figure 6. *Flame squib.*

Pressure squib

The pressure squib, Figure 7, generates 200 to 500 psi in a closed 16.4-cm³ bomb in less than 20 milliseconds. Its size and external appearance are the same as those of the flame squib except that it has four instead of two lead wires.

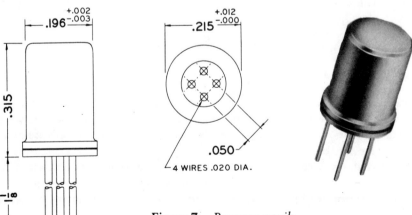

Figure 7. *Pressure squib.*

High temperature primer

The high temperature primer, shown in Figure 8, is exceptionally reliable and operates up to 350 °F.

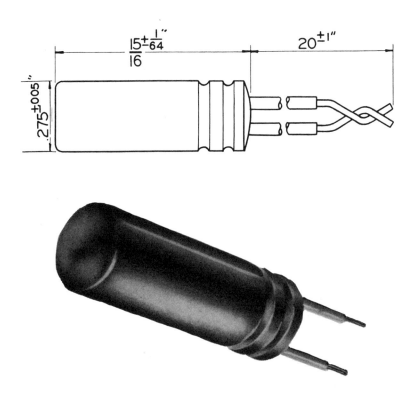

Gasless squib

Development of the gasless squib was a response to the requirement of devices such as the Safe Destroyer for igniting a composition in a sealed system. The model in Figure 9 has a bare bridge wire to convert the electric current to heat for igniting the surrounding mix. Depending on the composition to be ignited, the bridge wire may be coated with a gasless first fire to make it more sensitive. One base mix consists of a 70:30 mix of Fe_2O_3 and Ti. A first-fire coating bead can be made of 50% Fe_2O_3, 20% Pb_3O_4, and 30% Ti, bound with a cellulose acetate-acetone solution.

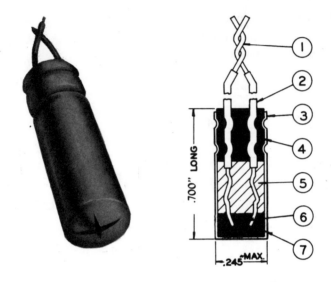

Figure 9. *Gasless or instantaneous squib.* 1. *Twisted leads kept shorted until use.* 2. *Straight leads emerging from squib.* 3. *Metal case.* 4. *Sealed base.* 5. *Gasless or instantaneous base mix as required.* 6. *Bridge wire.* 7. *First fire.*

Instantaneous squib

The instantaneous squib is the same as the gasless squib except that the mix it contains may consist of either 33:67 TiH_2-$KClO_4$ or 40:60 Zr-$KClO_4$. Both these mixes explode violently when ignited, undergoing true detonation themselves, and can be used to detonate high explosives.

TOURBILLON

The tourbillon (French for vortex or whirlwind) originated in France in the early nineteenth century as a piece of fireworks and was revived in the United States in the late 1940s as the *Flying Saucer* or *Whirly Bird.* It also has military applications.

The tourbillon is a cylindrical tube, press-loaded with a rocket composition and sealed at both ends. Holes are drilled into the body on opposite sides, as shown in Figure 10, just below the central axis, and a metal or plastic propeller is attached to the "top" between the two holes. When ignited, the rocket composition emits opposing jets through the holes, causing rotation. The rotating propeller lifts the spinning tube. Most commercial tourbillons have only one hole, which is all that is needed for simple rotation, but military types usually have two holes.

Figure 10. *Tourbillon. Spin from side exhausts and lift from propeller create a rising spiral movement.*

DIMPLE MOTOR

The dimple motor has a recess (dimple) in its free end which pops outward as shown in Figure 11 when the internal mix is ignited and builds up pressure. The protruding tip then makes an electrical contact to complete a circuit, or presses against a nearby part to instigate mechanical action.

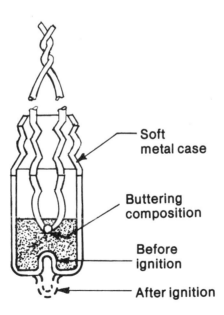

Soft
metal case

Buttering
composition

Before
ignition

After ignition

Figure 11. *Dimple motor.*

BELLOWS MOTOR

The case of the bellows motor before ignition is collapsed in close accordion folds as shown in Figure 12. Ignition extends the case. The bellows motor performs the same functions as the dimple motor with the added feature that it can curve around a corner.

Cohn[9] discussed the dimple and bellows motors, as well as two others called the Rotact Motor and the Piston Motor, in a paper presented to the 12th Annual Symposium on Behavior and Utilization of Explosives in Engineering Design held at the University of New Mexico in 1972.

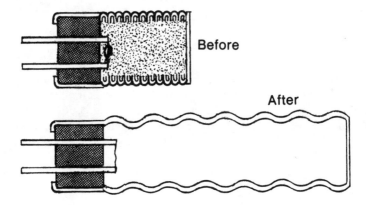

Figure 12. *Bellows motor.*

SEPARATIONS

Pyrotechnics devices can also be used to cause mechanical separation.

Frangible Bolts

Frangible bolts have sufficient strength to hold an assembly together until actuation causes them to disintegrate and allow the assembly to fall apart.

Shear Pins

Many base-ejection artillery and aerial shells are required to open and expel their contents. This is accomplished by attaching the base plate to the shell with pins placed so that an impulse from inside the shell severs the connection.

Fusible Linkages

These serve a purpose similar to that of frangible bolts but separate by melting when heated.

Guillotine Cutter

The guillotine cutter is a poised knife blade mounted in a slot and cuts a halyard or cable when propelled by an ignited pyrotechnic composition.

Other ingenious applications of pyrotechnically instigated motion can be found in Brauer[10] and Moses[11].

The materials of action are variable but the use we make of them should be constant.

Epictetus

CHAPTER IX

REFERENCES

1. Davis, T.L., *The Chemistry of Powder and Explosives,* Wiley, New York, 1941.
2. Van Gelder, A.P. and Schlatter, H., *History of the Explosives Industry in America,* Columbia University Press, New York, 1927.
3. Pawlak, D.E. and Levenson, M., U.S. Patent 4,128,443 (1978).
4. Stine, G.H., *Handbook of Model Rocketry,* 4th ed., Follett, Chicago, 1976.
5. *Chem. Abs.* **88,** 107545a (1978).
6. Doin, B., Cord, P.P., and Pasquiery, M., *Chem. Abs.* **87,** 103983y (1977).
7. MacSenzie, G.L., U.S. Patent Application 456,703.
8. McCulloch, C.R., U.S. Patent Application 445,383.
9. Cohn, G., in *12th Annual Symposium on Behavior and Utilization of Explosives in Engineering Design,* University of New Mexico, Albuquerque, 1972, pp. 189-200.
10. Brauer, K.O., *Handbook of Pyrotechnics,* Chemical Publishing Co., New York, 1974.
11. Moses, S.A., *Explosive Components for Aerospace Systems, op. cit.* in reference 8, pp. 235-242.

Chapter X

NOISE

And all the people saw the thunderings, and the light-
nings, and the noise . . .

Exodus 20:18

Since the thirteenth century when Friar Roger Bacon gave directions for making "a thundering noise and bright flash,"[1] and Albertus Magnus prepared a powder to "create thunder and lightning," noise and pyrotechnics have always gone together. However, noise was just the byproduct of some other effect (except for the special case of fireworks treated in the next chapter).

If we consider the noise that results from an explosion and try to define "explosion," we find the definition more elusive than one might think. Various encyclopedias and dictionaries give the following:

"A violent expansion of a substance accompanied by a sudden release of energy. The cause may be a very rapid chemical reaction, or the bursting out of gases or vapours under pressure, as from a steam boiler."[2]

"A sudden outburst of gas and heat, thereby exerting high pressures on its surroundings."[3]

"Any sudden or violent expansion process which yields a high volume of gases with shattering effect on their environment."[4]

"A violent expansion or bursting with a noise as of gunpowder or a boiler—the noise itself."[5]

Strangely, only the last quotation uses the word "noise." For the purposes of this chapter at least, noise must be part of the definition of "explosion." Based on the above definitions, perhaps the easiest compromise is "A sudden release of chemical energy with noise." Unfortunately, this excludes cork pop-guns, the sudden perforation of paper, the clapping of an inflated paper bag, and the unvented can of beans in the campfire. It also seems to exclude nuclear explosions (fission and fusion). However, all these explosions have in common the creation of a sonic effect by disturbance of the surrounding gas molecules. Thus, confinement of the energy source contributes to the suddenness of the process and the loudness of the noise.

Simulacra

The M80 firecracker is used to simulate machine-gun fire in the training of troops. It is a spirally wound chipboard tube, about 0.5 inch in inside diameter by 1¼ inch in length, with an outer ply of Kraft paper and a charge of about 2.5 g of either 4:1:1 $KClO_4$-Al-Sb_2S_3 or a 50:50 Sb_2S_3S- mix. The common name for the mix is *flash and sound*.

During loading, one end of the M80 is sealed with a paper cap and the charge is introduced. If the perchlorate mix is used, a premix of dark pyro-grade Al powder and Sb_2S_3 is inserted first and then freshly micropulverized and dried $KClO_4$ is placed on the premix. The other end of the tube is then sealed with sodium silicate, sawdust, and chalk or with another paper cap. Loaded tubes are then "rumbled" for 15 to 20 minutes in a barrel containing some dry sawdust, thus mixing the ingredients in the M80 package with minimal exposure of personnel to the hazards of the very dangerous composition. After mixing, the side of each tube is punctured and a length of fireworks fuse is inserted and cemented in place.

A new Japanese *flash and sound* mix[6], patented in 1975, eliminates the Al:

	%
$KClO_4$	45
KNO_3	5
Potassium picrate	28
Salicylic acid	22

Ellern[7] also describes pyrotechnic simulators for projectile airburst and groundburst, gunflash, booby-trap flash, an atomic bomb explosion, and a tank-gun firing.

WHISTLES

The projectile groundburst and booby-trap flash simulators precede their flash and explosion with a whistling sound. The fact that certain compositions whistle when compressed into a tube and ignited has been used in the fireworks industry for many years. Picrate compositions were the first whistle mixes used in the United States, and another old formulation was a combination of gallic acid and $KClO_3$. The origin of these whistle mixes and the discovery of their peculiar properties are obscure. However, Maxwell[8] has studied pyrotechnic whistles extensively and written the definitive treatise on their behavior and probable mechanism of sound production.

Maxwell made most of his measurements with a 70:30 $KClO_4$-potassium benzoate mix, but also investigated mixes of 60:40 potassium picrate-KNO_3, 25:75 gallic acid-$KClO_3$, and 70:30 potassium dinitrophenate-KNO_3. His most important findings are depicted in Figures 1 through 5.

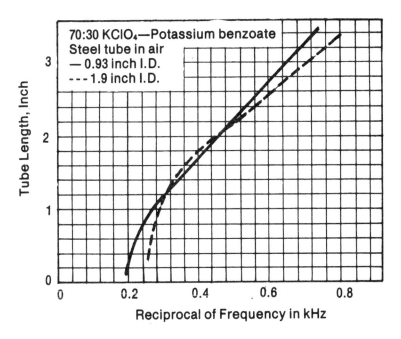

Figure 1. *Effect of open tube length on whistle frequency*[8].

Figure 1 shows that the frequency of the main component of the sound falls continuously as the length of the tube above the burning surface increases. Maxwell constructed a constant-frequency whistle by applying the "coachman's lamp" principle. He used a telescoping case with the upper portion resting on a shoulder of the burning mix. As the mix was consumed, the upper case descended, maintaining a constant "throat." Figure 2 shows that the mix burns faster at higher whistle frequencies, and burns fastest if not constrained to whistle at all.

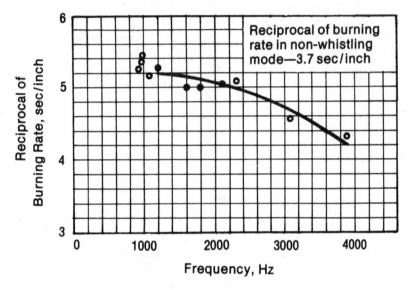

Figure 2. *Effect of whistle frequency on burning rate*[8].

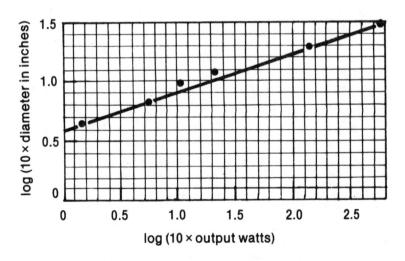

Figure 3. *Effect of whistle diameter on acoustic output*[8].

Acoustic output (Figure 3) increases somewhat faster than the cube of the diameter. Maximum acoustic output for the $KClO_4$-benzoate system, as indicated in Figure 4, occurs at critical proportions of the ingredients. The proportions do not produce the maximum burning rate but correspond closely to stoichiometry for the reaction:

$$15KClO_4 + 4KOOC \cdot C_6H_5 \cdot 3H_2O \rightarrow 26CO_2 + 15KCl + 2K_2CO_3$$

This is a mix of 70.8% $KClO_4$ and 29.2% potassium benzoate.

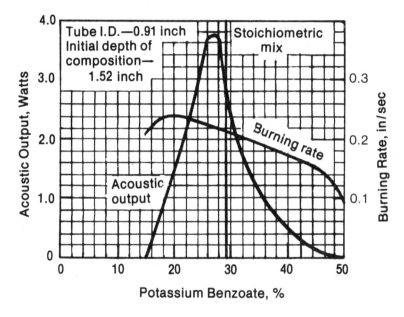

Figure 4. *Effect of whistle composition on acoustic output and burning rate*[8].

Picrate-KNO_3 proportions for maximum sound were less critical. The commercial production process at the Kent Manufacturing Corporation, Chestertown, Maryland consisted of bringing water to a boil with live steam in a 55-gallon drum; stirring in picric acid to saturation; adding small increments of solid K_2CO_3 and stirring until effervescence ceased; stirring in an amount of KNO_3 equal to about one-third the weight of picric acid; then cooling and filtering the solution. KNO_3 additions to the hot potassium picrate solution enhanced crystallization by means of the salting-out and common-ion effects. The resulting crystalline meal was dried and gave good results in whistle devices.

Figure 5 shows that the burning rate of the whistle mix decreases as the surrounding pressure falls.

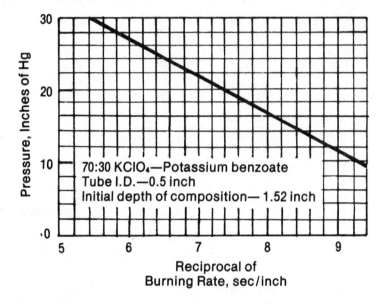

Figure 5. *Effect of pressure on whistle burning rate*[8].

Maxwell observed that "A whistling composition burns intermittently. Everytime the surface is ignited, a wave passes down the tube and is reflected as a wave of rarefaction from the open end. This wave of rarefaction strikes the surface of the composition where it is reflected without change of phase, i.e., as a wave of condensation, and travels down to the surface of the composition." He suggests "that the mechanism of combustion . . . involves the explosion of crystals as an essential part of the process. If the composition is not contained in a suitable tube, these crystals will explode in random fashion and the products of combustion will flow from the surface at a uniform rate and no definite note or indeed any sound of appreciable intensity will result. If, however, the composition is contained in a suitable resonating tube, the flame will be forced in and out of the surface by alternate waves of compression and rarefaction and every time it is forced into the surface a fresh mass of crystals will explode."

Maxwell's hypothesis was tested by an addition of 3% metal powder (Cu or Fe) to the perchlorate-benzoate mix to enable the flame front to travel more quickly[9]. The metal additions produced shriller, i.e., higher-frequency, whistles, supporting the hypothesis.

One problem with the whistle mixes investigated by Maxwell is their sensitivity to accidental or premature detonation. Ellern[7] gives the formula for the reputedly safer official U.S. mix: 72.5% $KClO_4$, 27.5% sodium salicylate. However, this author knows of two high-order explosions definitely caused by the salicylate whistle mix. Probably, high order explosions are an inherent risk with all whistle mixes. The physiological hazards associated with the picrate mix, however, may outweigh the explosion hazard. Not only does it cause long-lasting skin discoloration, but its dust is extremely irritating.

EXPLODING NOISEMAKERS

Booby traps

The *Booby Trap* is a novel noise-making device once imported by the U.S. fireworks industry. It is an offshoot of the *Party Popper.* It consists of a paper-wrapped length of woven cotton thread looped at the center to hold a bead of toy-cap mix, as pictured in Figure 6. In production, the paper is moistened with paste and laid flat; the looped string is positioned on the paper; a drop of wet mix is placed in the loop; and the string is then wrapped and the assembly is dried. Suddenly pulling the ends of the string away from each other causes the cap mix to explode. Four possible cap mixes are:

	1 %	2 %	3 %	4 %
$KClO_3$	81	68	67	78
Red phosphorus	8	12	27	12
Sulfur	5.5	9	3	
Precipitated chalk	5.5	11	3	10

The first three mixes are from Ellern[7], listed under Armstrong's Mixture on page 353.

Figure 6. Booby Trap *novelty noisemaker.*

The fireworks industry voluntarily banned importation of the *Booby Trap* into the United States after a case was dropped and caused an explosion that triggered the detonation of other cases.

Snap'n Pops

Snap'n Pops, also called *Devil Bangs,* are interesting and innocuous noise makers first introduced into the United States about five years ago from Brazil. They are also made in Korea. A *Snap'n Pop* is a cigarette paper rolled and twisted into the shape of a roughly spherical teardrop with a tail. The teardrop is loaded with about 0.18 g of small gravel or coarse sand coated with 0.0008 g of a silver compound. When the device is thrown against a hard surface, friction between the granules sets off the silver compound with a small, quick bang.

The silver compound is variously represented as the azide, AgN_3, or the fulminate, $Ag_2(CNO)_2$, but the following description of its preparation leaves no doubt that it is the fulminate:

> A nitric acid solution of silver nitrate is mixed with alcohol and allowed to react for approximately 15 minutes. The subsequent white precipitate is then filtered off and allowed to air-dry for 24 hours. This pyrotechnic silver compound is mixed with washed, screened, river gravel and a small quantity wrapped in thin paper to produce a tear-shaped drop approximately 1/4" in diameter and 3/4" long.[10]

This description correlated closely to the directions in Weingart[11] for preparing silver fulminate for silver torpedos: -

> ... take 8 ounces of C. P. nitric acid (42%) and add 2 ounces of water gradually, stirring constantly with a glass rod. Into this put a silver dollar (or 1 ounce of metallic silver). Warm slightly until a brisk reaction takes place. When the silver is completely dissolved allow the solution to cool for 3 minutes. Then add 16 ounces of pure alcohol. Add it all at once quickly and be sure that the vessel containing the solution of silver is quite large because a violent effervescence will take place. After it subsides add 3 more ounces of alcohol. Let stand for 1/4 to 1/2 hour. A white crystalline precipitate will be found on the bottom of the vessel. This is the fulminate and may be collected on a filter and dried in a shady place.

This small novelty is safe in storage, shipment, and use. A study by the author resulted in the following observations:

> The noise is much less than that of toy paper caps and the small explosion is produced far from the user.

> Operation generates little flame and almost no gas compared with

Party Poppers or toy caps, so that the granules are not widely scattered even if the wrapper tears.

Except for the paper wrap, they are nonflammable.

Detonation in a vapor of diethyl or petroleum ether caused no ignition.

Two hours of heating in a 75 °C oven did not set it off.

Even when it goes off while being handled, it causes no burn, tingle, or damage.

Railway torpedoes

The need to warn a locomotive engineer of impending danger ahead has given rise to another noise maker, the *Railway Torpedo*. It consists of a bound and shaped mixture of $KClO_3$, S, sand (between 50 and 100 mesh), and chalk, packaged in waterproof paper and equipped with lead or aluminum straps to hold it in place on the rail. Noise level and heat, water, and impact resistance are closely specified by the Bureau of Explosives, Association of American Railroads. Tenney L. Davis[12] cites $KClO_4$-Sb_2S_3-S mixes for *Railway Torpedos* in a 6:5:1 and a 12:9:3 ratio.

Salutes

Protocol still demands that visiting celebrities receive a welcoming salute, the number of guns fired rising with the visitor's rank and importance. The blank shells used are generally loaded with black powder and sealed with a waxed-cardboard press-fitted plug.

Starting Guns and Toy Cannon

Starting guns are traditionally indispensable for races, and toy cannons are perennially popular noise makers. The sailboat regattas in tidewater Maryland have a starting gun for each heat of each class and another to announce the finishing lap. The guns use cartridges that look like shotgun shells and are filled with black powder. Dwindling of the number of black-powder manufacturers may endanger the continued use of starting guns.

Here once the embattled farmers stood
And fired the shot heard round the world.
R. W. Emerson

Chapter X

REFERENCES

1. Van Gelder, A.P. and Schlatter, H., *History of the Explosives Industry in America*, Columbia University Press, New York, 1927.
2. *Encyclopedia Brittanica,* Preece, W.E., Ed., Encyclopedia Brittanica, Chicago, 1975.
3. *Collier's Encyclopedia,* MacMillan, New York.
4. *Encyclopedia International,* Grolier, New York, 1976.
5. *The American College Dictionary,* Random House, New York, 1947.
6. Japanese Patent 7,504,724 (1975).
7. Ellern, H., *Military and Civilian Pyrotechnics,* Chemical Publishing Co., New York, 1968.
8. Maxwell, W.R., in *4th Symposium (International) on Combustion,* Williams and Wilkins, Baltimore, 1953.
9. Biddle, H.O., Senior Thesis, Washington College, Chestertown, Md., 1968.
10. Report of visit to the factory of Fabrica de Estados de Salao Tamoio Ltda. by an inspector of the Sociedad Brasilera de Superintendencia.
11. Weingart, G.W., *Pyrotechnics,* 2nd ed., Chemical Publishing Co., New York, 1947, p. 174.
12. Davis, T.L., *The Chemistry of Powder and Explosives,* Wiley, New York, 1941.

Chapter XI

FIREWORKS

The day will be the most memorable in the history of America. I am apt to believe that it will be celebrated by succeeding generations as the great anniversary festival . . . It ought to be solemnized with pomp and parade . . . bonfires and illuminations from one end of this continent to the other, from this time forward forevermore.

John Adams, July 3, 1776

Not long ago, the writer of these lines,
In the mad pride of intellectuality,
Maintained 'the power of words'—denied that ever
A thought arose within the human brain
Beyond the utterance of the human tongue . . . .

Edgar Allan Poe

Certainly the most noted and widely viewed application of the principles of pyrotechnics and solid state chemistry is the annual 4th-of-July fireworks display to celebrate America's independence. As Poe says in the above quotation, " . . . the utterance of the human tongue . . . " is not always adequate to express what the human brain can think; so do words fail to do justice to the mixture of wonder, enchantment, and joy that lights up the faces of children watching a fireworks show. Their eyes emit almost palpable expressions of pleasure and glee. Surely, the longevity of the fireworks industry owes much to the thrilling effect fireworks have on children of all ages.

When frequently asked, with a condescending tone, "What good are fireworks?", the author's rejoinder has been, "What good are the Mona Lisa or the Pieta?" Such an exchange can apply to almost any form of amusement or art. Disparagers have yet to make a convincing reply.

Approximately 150 firms are now engaged in the manufacture, import, and distribution of fireworks in the United States, and many other companies are active in retail sales and firing of public displays. The American Pyrotechnics Association, the trade organization of the fireworks industry, estimates that U.S. retail sales of fireworks reached $100,000,000 in 1979.

About 25% of the fireworks used in the United States are produced domestically, significantly less than in previous decades. The rest is imported, primarily from the Peoples Republic of China which quickly dominated the import market after resumption of U.S.-China trade in 1972 and also introduced a variety of new items. Imports also come from Japan, Taiwan, Hong Kong, Macao, France, Brazil, Korea, England, India, and Germany.

The right of the public to buy and use fireworks is a controversial and emotional issue in some areas of the United States. This led to an investigation in the early 1970s by the United States Consumer Product Safety Commission (CPSC) and the development of stringent regulations covering the devices[1]. To a request for a total ban on public fireworks use, the CPSC replied:

> These interested parties generally maintained that all fireworks are too dangerous to be used by individuals and that, in addition to causing injuries and property damage, fireworks creates unwarranted noise and air pollution. However, none of these parties provided data in support of the position that all fireworks are too dangerous to be used by individuals and the Commission is unaware of any information or data available from other sources sufficient to warrant a total ban on all types of fireworks.

Also, in his report on the public hearing, CPSC Administration Law Judge Paul Pfeiffer concluded:

> There is considerable credible evidence to the effect that relatively few injuries occur in states which permit at least some form of fireworks, where the citizenry has become experienced and somewhat skilled in their use.

Since the enactment of their safety regulations in 1976, CPSC has maintained a policy of "Celebrate, but Safely" and has continually stressed safety education.

In Great Britain, the Reverend Ronald Lancaster stated in his excellent book on fireworks:[2]

From time to time attempts are made to ban the sale of fireworks to the public. Recent voting in Great Britain indicated that the majority of the voters were against such a move, and quite rightly so. After all, people have to act responsibly and should be free to exercise their responsibility in this direction. Britain, in common with most European countries, has rigid legislation and inspection of firework manufacture and an agreement amongst manufacturers that flash crackers and certain dangerous fireworks should not be sold to the general public. The result is that a fairly wide range of fireworks can be purchased in the shops at certain times of the year, and display fireworks can be organized by people with specialized experience. The U. S. A. could do well to benefit from our experience, for it would appear that a country priding itself on its freedom can nevertheless allow some bureaucratic fire marshal or other excited group to bring in legislation to outlaw fireworks in individual states. The result appears to be that it encourages people to buy fireworks over the border in a more permissive state and fire them illegally. Restrict the dangerous explosive items by all means, but "safe and sane" as the Americans put it, covers very much more than sparklers.

The controversy reflects the existence of a zero-risk philosophy which may be shortsighted, unrealistic, and unnecessarily timid. For example, when a movement started in 1971 to outlaw sparklers, the record demonstrated that a total of 300 accidents had occurred in the use of some 100,000,000 sparklers, indicating that they could be described as 99.9997% safe. This proves that the design is certainly not inherently hazardous. Design alone cannot prevent malicious or foolhardy use.

BRIEF HISTORY OF U.S. FIREWORKS

Fireworks, as did all other pyrotechnics, began with the development of black powder, that fascinating blend of KNO_3, S, and charcoal (see Chapter IX). The 75:15:10 ingredients ratio has not changed much over the past 400 years, nor has the manufacturing process undergone much modification. Black powder production remains extremely hazardous and plant design must take into account the assumption that unexpected explosions will occur.

Although black powder is generally believed to have appeared first in China, pioneers in its development as a propellant (hence the invention of the rocket) also included India, Italy, France, England, and Germany. Progression to explosives and the creation of firecrackers soon followed when it was discovered that black powder produced noise if ignited while confined in a sealed tube.

The American black-powder industry developed early, one mill opening in Milton, Massachusetts about 1675 and others appearing soon thereafter. However, limited output due to accidental explosions in the mills, government restrictions, and severe competition from imported powder caused George Washington to write to the Continental Congress in 1775 about the alarming black-powder shortage in the colonies. Fortunately, a few domestic plants managed to begin producing powder which, augmented by imports from France, enabled the colonial army to win the Revolutionary War.

Manufacturing progress was rapid in the 1800s as E.I. du Pont, a young French immigrant, decided against a career in land development and went into the black-powder business. Setting up a factory on the Brandywine Creek near Wilmington, Delaware, young du Pont devoted careful attention to the purity of his starting materials and soon produced an excellent powder, comparable to the best in Europe.

However, the development of smokeless powder and the rise of the modern explosives industry had drastically reduced the demand for black powder by the early years of the twentieth century, with military applications and fireworks composing the bulk of the residual market. Many factories ceased production, to the point where the Goex factory in Moosic, Pennsylvania (formerly the E.I. du Pont de Nemours Belin plant) was the only remaining domestic black-powder producer in 1979.

As the black-powder industry developed in the United States, an infant fireworks industry emerged, with many European immigrants, particularly from Italy, providing the expertise necessary to safely manufacture high-quality fireworks. Most early items primarily produced noise, but as the modern chemical industry grew during the 1800s and early 1900s, and new chemicals that created spectacular color effects became available, the fireworks industry shifted toward color and other visual effects and away from simple noise.

August Hummel, a native of Augsburg, Germany who founded the Hummel and Robinson Company in 1913, immeasurably aided the U.S. fireworks industry with his wisdom and foresight as well as with chemical supplies. Specializing in pyrotechnic-grade chemicals, the company continues today in South Plainfield, New Jersey as the Hummel Chemical Company under the guidance of Mr. Hummel's son-in-law, James M. Vreeland.

For years, the Hummel company was the only source of high-grade $Ba(NO_3)_2$, $Sr(NO_3)_2$, KNO_3, $KClO_3$, $KClO_4$, and dark *pyro* Al. August Hummel was a one-man research and development department, visiting Germany,

Italy, and Spain yearly to obtain samples of new products and making available to the fireworks industry new or improved chemical compositions that made possible more spectacular effects.

The fireworks industry has always been a valuable resource for national defense. Many factories converted from fireworks to production of defense material during World War II and the Korean conflict and several received outstanding-achievement awards. Fireworks workers quickly learned safe ways to handle hazardous materials which they could readily apply to ordnance.

Triumph Explosives of Elkton, Maryland is a good example. Benjamin Decker founded Triumph in the 1920s as a fireworks factory and has since trained thousands of employees. Decker was an imaginative man, with boundless energy and enthusiasm, and was responsible for many modernizations such as the first fireworks safety-fuse machine and automatic cone rollers.

"Uncle Bennie," as he was affectionately known, brought the Nocke family (makers of non-mercuric *snakes*) and the Wahners (picrate whistles) to America to increase his product line. He also tapped the mechanical wizardry of Franklin Johnson and his son Jack. (The Johnson family's collective brilliance is evident throughout the pyrotechnic community in their toggle presses, candle, rocket, and fireworks fuse machines, fuse cutters, and powder measurers, loaders, and pressers still in use today.) Under Decker's leadership, this small cadre of skilled pyrotechnicians successfully undertook the complete loading and assembly of 40-mm rounds during World War II. It was at Triumph that experienced fireworks people such as Roland Meekins, Bill Franklin, Joe Weber, and Bill Corriden took a young Army captain and gave him a short but intensive apprenticeship in mixing, granulating, pelleting, and "straight line" loading. At the close of the war, Triumph Explosives had expanded to over 10,000 employees.

Patrick Lizza accomplished a similar feat in Saugus, California. He turned Bermite Powder, a small fireworks factory, into a large and efficient producer of 20-mm ammunition.

Many of the early U.S. fireworks companies established in the 1800s and early 1900s remain active today under third and fourth generation descendants of the founders. Names like Lizza, Rozzi, Grucci, Fabrizi, Zambelli, and Vitale still produce high-quality items.

FIREWORKS CLASSIFICATION

Fireworks sold and used in the United States are divided into two main categories, common and special, subject to different regulations.

Common Fireworks

Common fireworks are small items containing small quantities of pyrotechnic chemicals and intended for individual use in backyard displays. At least some forms can be sold legally in 35 of the 50 states. The U.S. Department of Transportation (DOT) classifies them as Class C explosives[3]. The following are the DOT categories with size and powder-content limits. These common fireworks must comply with the safety standards of the U.S. Consumer Product Safety Commission.

COMMON FIREWORK. Small firework, designed primarily to produce visible effects by combustion, that must comply with the construction, chemical composition, and labeling regulations promulgated by the U.S. Consumer Product Safety Commission [CFR Title 16 - Commercial Practices, Part 1507]. Some small devices designed to produce an audible effect are included, such as whistling devices, ground devices containing 50 mg or less of explosive composition, and aerial devices containing 130 mg or less of explosive composition. Propelling or expelling charges consisting of a mixture of charcoal, sulfur, and potassium nitrate are not considered as designed to produce an audible effect. Common fireworks include the following:

A. Ground and hand-held sparkling devices

Dipped stick, wire sparkler. Stick or wire coated with pyrotechnic composition that produces a shower of sparks upon ignition. Total pyrotechnic composition may not exceed 100 g per item. Those devices containing any chlorate or perchlorate salts are not to exceed 5 g in total composition per item. Wire sparklers which contain no magnesium and which contain less than 100 g of composition per item are *not* included in this category, in accordance with the regulations of the U.S. Department of Transportation.

Cylindrical fountain. Cylindrical tube not exceeding 3/4 inch in inside diameter containing up to 75 g of pyrotechnic composition. Fountains produce a shower of color and sparks upon ignition, and sometimes a whistling effect. Cylindrical fountains may contain a spike to be inserted in the ground (spike fountain), a wooden or plastic base to be placed on the ground (base fountain), or a wooden or cardboard handle for items designed to be handheld (handle fountain).

Cone fountain. Cardboard or heavy paper cone containing up to 50 g of pyrotechnic composition. The effect is the same as that of a cylindrical fountain.

Illuminating torch. Cylindrical tube containing up to 100 g of pyrotechnic composition. Upon ignition, colored fire is produced. These may be either spike, base, or handle-type devices.

Wheel. Pyrotechnic device attached to a post or tree by means of a nail or string. Wheel contains up to six "driver" units—tubes not exceeding 1/2 inch in inside diameter that may contain up to 60 g of composition per driver unit.

Upon ignition, the wheel revolves, producing a shower of color and sparks and sometimes a whistling effect.

Ground spinner. Small device similar to wheels in design and effect, that is placed on the ground and ignited. A shower of sparks and color is produced by the rapidly spinning device.

Flitter sparkler. Narrow paper tube filled with pyrotechnic composition that produces color and sparks upon ignition. These devices do not use a fuse for ignition. The paper at one end of the tube is ignited to make the device function.

B. Aerial devices

Sky rocket. Tube not exceeding 1/2 inch in inside diameter that may contain up to 20 g of pyrotechnic composition. Sky rockets contain a wooden stick for guidance and stability and rise into the air upon ignition. A burst of color or noise or both is produced at the height of flight.

Missile-type rocket. Device similar to a sky rocket in size, composition, and effect that uses fins rather than a stick for guidance and stability.

Helicopter, aerial spinner. A tube not exceeding 1/2 inch in inside diameter that may contain up to 20 g of pyrotechnic composition. Some type of propeller or blade device is attached, and upon ignition the rapidly spinning device lifts into the air. A visible or audible effect is produced at the height of flight.

Roman candle. Heavy paper or cardboard tube not exceeding 3/8 inch in inside diameter that contains up to 20 g of pyrotechnic composition. Upon ignition, up to ten "stars" (pellets of pressed pyrotechnic composition that burn with bright color) are individually expelled at several-second intervals.

Mine, shell. Heavy cardboard or paper tube up to 2-1/2 inch in inside diameter with a wooden or plastic base attached, containing up to 40 g of pyrotechnic composition. Upon ignition, "stars" (see Roman Candle), firecrackers (see Ground Audible Devices below), whistles, parachutes, or combinations of these effects are propelled into the air, with the tube remaining on the ground.

C. Ground audible devices

Firecracker, salute. Small paper-wrapped or cardboard tube that may not contain more than 50 mg of pyrotechnic composition. Noise, accompanied by a flash of light, is produced upon ignition.

Chaser. Small paper or cardboard tube that travels along the ground upon ignition. A whistling effect is often produced, and a small noise may be produced. The explosive composition used to create the noise may not exceed 50 mg.

D. Combination items

Fireworks devices containing combinations of two or more of the effects described in the preceding categories.

NOVELTIES AND TRICK NOISEMAKERS. Small devices also intended for individual use but not classified as common fireworks by the DOT.

A. Snake, glow worm. Pressed pellet of pyrotechnic composition that produces a large, snake-like ash upon burning. The ash expands in length as the pellet burns. These devices may not contain any mercuric compounds.

B. Smoke device. Tube or sphere containing pyrotechnic composition that produces white or colored smoke upon ignition as the primary effect.

C. Wire sparkler. Wire coated with pyrotechnic composition that produces a shower of sparks upon ignition. These items may *not* contain magnesium and must not exceed 100 g of composition per item. Devices containing any chlorate or perchlorate salts may not exceed 5 g of composition per item.

D. Trick noisemaker. Item that produces a small report intended to surprise the user. These devices include:

a. *Party popper.* Small plastic or paper item containing not in excess of 16 mg of explosive composition that is friction sensitive. A string protruding from the device is pulled to ignite it, expelling paper streamers and producing a small report.

b. *Booby trap.* Small tube with string protruding from both ends, similar to a party popper in design. The ends of this string are pulled to ignite the friction sensitive composition, producing a small report.

c. *Snapper.* Small, paper-wrapped item containing a minute quantity of explosive composition (silver fulminate) coated on small bits of sand. When dropped, the device explodes, producing a small report.

d. *Trick match.* Kitchen or book match that has been coated with a small quantity of explosive or pyrotechnic composition. Upon ignition of the match, a small report or shower of sparks is produced.

e. *Cigarette load.* Small wooden peg that has been coated with a small quantity of explosive composition (lead azide). Upon ignition of a cigarette containing one of the pegs, a small report is produced.

f. *Auto burglar alarm.* Tube which contains pyrotechnic composition that produces a loud whistle and/or smoke when ignited. A small quantity of explosive, not exceeding 50 mg, may also be used to produce a small report. A squib is used to ignite the device.

Special fireworks

In contrast to common backyard fireworks, special fireworks are intended to be fired by trained personnel in carefully selected shooting areas. The DOT classifies them as Class B explosives. They are now legal in all 50 states, but the DOT and the Bureau of Alcohol, Tobacco and Firearms subject their transport, storage, purchase, and use to stricter regulations than are applied to common fireworks.

Some special fireworks, such as large wheels, skyrockets, and fountains, are oversized versions of common fireworks. However, there are two unique special fire works: the aerial shell and the set piece.

Aerial shells. To many people, the aerial shell exploding high in the sky into a floral shower of color and sparks is the ultimate achievement of the pyrotechnic art. Some are small enough to fit the common fireworks category, but those containing more than 40 g of pyrotechnic charge are classified as special fireworks.

Aerial shells are either spherical or cylindrical. Diameters commonly range from 2 to 8 inches, but occasionally may be 10, 12, or even 24 inches. George Plimpton and the staff of the New York Pyrotechnic Products Company of Bellport, New York recently strove for a new world's record by firing a 40-inch shell.

Japanese and Chinese factories generally make spherical aerial shells, while American factories almost exclusively make cylindrical types. Spherical shells, which require considerably more time to manufacture, contain a symmetrical arrangement of star pellets that produces a characteristic pyrotechnic blossom resembling a huge chrysanthemum or peony.

Aerial shells are fired from a metal or heavy-paper mortar securely buried in earth or sand or anchored to a sturdy wooden rack. After the shell is inserted into the mortar, a length of fuse protrudes which is lit by hand with a fusee or cigar or ignited remotely by means of an electric squib to launch the firework. The burning fuse first ignites a charge of coarse (usually FF) black powder which propels the shell several hundred feet into the air. The shell must fit the mortar snugly to allow gases from the burning black powder to build up adequate lifting pressure. Simultaneously as the shell leaves the mortar, a delay fuse is lit, timed to ignite the main body of pyrotechnic powder at the peak of the shell's flight. This bursting charge of KNO_3, S, and charcoal ruptures the shell and ignites the load of stars, whistles, salutes, and other items packed into the casing.

Multi-break shells, a favorite with spectators, consist of several cylinders in a single outer housing. Rupture of the first cylinder lights a delay fuse which ignites a second cylinder after a suitable interval. With more delay fuses and cylinders, a single shell can release a spectacular sequence of pyrotechnic events.

Set pieces. Set pieces are the designs and messages, such as the Liberty Bell, the Stars and Stripes, "Hello," or "Goodnight" without which no 4th-of-July fireworks display would be complete. They are constructed of lances (thin cardboard tubes loaded with color-producing composition) nailed or stapled to a wooden lattice in the desired pattern, and can be prepared well ahead of time. A pyrotechnic American flag would have lances with strontium nitrate (red), copper salts (blue), and Al or Mg (white).

The lances are interconnected with *quick match,* a special fuse made of cotton wicking impregnated with KNO_3-S-charcoal powder and enclosed in a loosely fitting paper sheath. The fuse burns at a moderate rate where it is uncovered. However, when the burning zone enters the paper sheath, the sheath confines and channels the gases, accelerating the burning rate so that the entire array of lances ignites almost at once and instantly creates the full luminous pattern in color. Only the artist's imagination limits the possibilities for set pieces.

FIREWORKS REGULATIONS

Common fireworks

Common fireworks must now comply with the safety standards of the U.S. Consumer Product Safety Commission.[4] (CPSC regulations do not apply to fireworks used in organized public displays.) Distributors in violation are subject to criminal penalties specified in the Federal Hazardous Substances Act. Some of the major sections of the CPSC regulations are as follows:

Labeling. The nature of the hazard, e.g., FLAMMABLE, EMITS SHOWERS OF SPARKS, and instructions for proper use must be clearly labeled on each item. Required wording for each of the Class C fireworks is specified.

Firecrackers. Firecracker-type devices containing more than 50 mg (0.77 grains) of explosive composition are banned (the previous maximum was 130 mg, or 2 grains). Aerial fireworks such as skyrockets and shells may still contain up to 130 mg of noisemaking material. The only exemptions from these limits are the larger firecrackers used in wildlife management programs administered by the U.S. Department of the Interior or an appropriate state or local agency.

Prohibited chemicals. The following sensitive, poisonous, or highly reactive chemicals are prohibited or limited for use in Class C fireworks:

Arsenic compounds
Mercury compounds
Boron
Magnesium (except as the Mg-Al alloy *magnalium*)
Titanium (when the particle size is less than 100 mesh)
Zirconium
Chlorates (except in certain small items in limited quantities and
    in certain colored smoke mixes, caps, and party poppers)
Gallates or gallic acid
Picrates or picric acid

Thiocyanates

Phosphorus (except red phosphorus in caps and party poppers)

Less hazardous substitutes are available to produce the desired pyrotechnic effect, e.g., perchlorates for chlorates and Al for Mg.

Fuses. Fuses must be coated or otherwise treated to reduce the chance of side instead of end ignition (by the user or a stray spark) and a consequent shortening of the burning time. The green, thread-wrapped American safety fuse, coated with a cellulose-acetate fuse dope, meets this requirement, but most Oriental twisted-paper fuses do not. Most Oriental manufacturers have now switched to the thread-wrapped powder fuse to comply with CPSC rules. Some small fireworks, such as small ground spinners and rockets, that contain less than 6 g of pyrotechnic chemicals and use a restricted orifice to develop the thrust needed for proper performance, are exempt from this fuse requirement.

Fuses should also burn at least 3 and no more than 6 seconds before igniting the firework. This should allow the operator time to retreat a safe distance after lighting the fuse and cause the firework to go off before an impatient operator is tempted to approach the firework to check if the fuse is still burning.

Base dimensions. To prevent tipping over of standing fireworks such as cone and cylinder fountains, which might spray spectators with sparks and stars, the horizontal dimensions of the bases or bottoms of Class C items must now equal at least one-third the height.

Burnout and blowout. The paper walls of such fireworks as fountains and Roman candles must be strong enough to contain the pressure generated by the burning composition. If the wall fails, burning material may spew out the side toward the operator or spectators rather than through the top. Burnout or blowout of the tube wall or bottom may also result from cavities or loose powder due to improper loading.

Toy smoke devices. Toy smoke devices must also be constructed to prevent burnout or blowout and must not produce an external flame during normal operation. To prevent possibly harmful mistakes, their color must not be the same as that of banned Class B explosive devices. Injuries have been reported related to dangerous devices, such as a cherry bomb, being mistaken for a smoke ball when dropped near an unsuspecting bystander. Thus, red smoke balls (resembling cherry bombs) and silver-tube smoke devices (resembling banned silver salutes) are forbidden.

Rockets with sticks. All rockets, including the bottle type, must have a straight, rigid stick to provide stable flight. Unstable or undirected flight has caused fires and injuries. Rockets must also comply with burnout and blowout regulations to insure ignition of the main charge high in the air rather than on the ground.

Other sections of the CPSC regulations cover pyrotechnic composition leakage from the package, handles, spikes, wheels, and party poppers.

Special fireworks

Special fireworks must not only be used by trained operators and meet stricter overall handling regulations, but interstate transactions involving special fireworks are also subject to the license and permit requirements of the U.S. Treasury Department's Bureau of Alcohol, Tobacco and Firearms (U.S. Code of Federal Regulations, Title 27, Part 181). In most states, the purchase and operation of special fireworks require state and/or local permits and frequently insurance coverage in addition to the federal permit. The National Fire Protection Association's Committee on Pyrotechnics has prepared a guide for the safe conduct of a public special fireworks display[5] which contains useful information for anyone having such responsibility.

Note: Although the CPSC restrictions on the use of certain unstable, toxic, or highly reactive chemicals does not prohibit their use in special fireworks, the U.S. DOT does require that these pyrotechnic mixes withstand a 48-hour 75 °C stability test without marked deterioration.

FIREWORKS CHEMICALS

Relatively few different chemicals are used to produce the large bulk of fireworks for the U.S. market compared with the large variety needed for military and specialized civilian pyrotechnics, e.g., in aerospace applications. The small number of chemicals selected for fireworks must meet certain criteria. The first is stability. Mixes must withstand moisture and moist atmospheres, and finished devices must have a shelf life of at least one year to allow for the lag between production and retail sale which centers around the 4th of July and New Year's Eve. They must also be relatively insensitive to shock and the wide range of temperatures encountered in shipping and storage. Fireworks materials must be readily available in bulk at reasonable prices to enable the manufacturer to compete with both domestic and overseas suppliers in a highly competitive market.

DOT shipping restrictions

Experience has shown certain pyrotechnic mixes to be inherently unstable and the U.S. Department of Transportation now forbids the shipping of the following:

Explosives or fireworks containing an ammonium salt and a chlorate (ammonium chlorate is very unstable)

Fireworks containing copper sulphate and a chlorate (copper chlorate is very unstable)

Firecrackers and salutes containing more than 12 grains (780 mg) each of explosive (a pack of many small items can mass detonate)

Fireworks containing yellow or white phosphorus

Fireworks or fireworks compositions that ignite spontaneously or markedly decompose when subjected to 75 °C (167 °F) for 48 consecutive hours

Oxidizers

Oxidizers supply the oxygen needed to drive the pyrotechnic reaction, usually without requiring supplements from the atmosphere. Consequently, suffocation methods are not suitable for fighting pyrotechnic fires. Techniques such as water dousing must be used that lower the temperature below that required for reaction. Commonly used fireworks oxidizers are:

KNO_3 $Ba(NO_3)_2$
$KClO_3$ $Ba(ClO_3)_2$
$KClO_4$ NH_4ClO_4
$Sr(NO_3)_2$

Fuels

Fuels are the materials oxidized, or combusted, to liberate the heat needed to produce the desired pyrotechnic effect. Common fuels include Al, Mg, Fe, S, and charcoal. S and Sb_2S_3 serve as tinders in many pyrotechnic mixes because they ignite easily and trigger pyrotechnic reactions among less reactive neighboring substances. As_2S_2 (Realgar) is also an effective tinder, but its toxicity precludes its use in common fireworks.

Binders

Most pyrotechnic mixes contain an organic polymer, activated by moistening, as a thickener and adhesive. The natural polymers, red gum and dextrine, are among the most commonly used, but newer synthetics such as the epoxies are becoming more popular. The advantage of synthetics is that their chemical behavior is more reproducible from batch to batch.

Special effects - Color

Other chemicals are added to the basic mix to produce desired colors, smoke, sound (e.g., a whistle), or motion. Bright, intense colors are a special challenge to the fireworks manufacturer since a compromise is often necessary between candlepower and color quality on the one hand and cost and chemical stability on the other. Blue is the most difficult color to produce at high candlepower. Paris Green is probably the best blue agent available, but its toxicity precludes its commercial use. The principal fireworks colors and the chemicals that produce them are shown in Table 1.

Table 1. Principal fireworks coloring agents

Red	$Sr(NO_3)_2$, $SrCO_3$
Green	$Ba(NO_3)_2$, $Ba(ClO_3)_2$
Yellow	$Na_2C_2O_4$, cryolite ($3NaF \cdot AlF_3$)
White	Mg, Al, Sb_2S_3
Blue	$CuCO_3$, Paris Green [$CuAs_2O_4 \cdot Cu(Ac)_2$], other Cu compounds

Table 2 gives specific color formulations that may stimulate other workers to develop new and better mixes.

Table 2. Formulas for colored fireworks

Blue	Parts	Japanese Blue	%	Japanese Blue	%
$KClO_4$	15	NH_4ClO_4	70	$KClO_4$	64
Stearic acid	1	$CuSO_4 \cdot 5H_2O$	10	Paris Green	17
Paris Green	4	Wood flour	10	Rosin	13
Shellac	1.5	Shellac	10	Dextrine	6
$CuSO_4 \cdot 5H_2O$	3				

Keystone Blue	Parts	Yellow Flare	%	Blue (Russian patent 394,345)	Parts
$KClO_4$	4	Mg	31	NH_4ClO_4	69-74
NH_4ClO_4	3	$KClO_4$	41	Urotropine	12-16
$CuCO_3$	1.5	$Na_2C_2O_4$	18	CuSCN	10-19
Red gum	1.5	Asphaltum	6	NC lacquer	1-4
Dextrine	0.5	Wet binder	5		

Violet (Russian patent 390,054)	Parts	Keystone Red	Parts	White Lance (Japanese)	%
NH_4ClO_4	40-8	$KClO_4$	35	NH_4ClO_4	40
$Sr(NO_3)_2$	8-12	$SrCO_3$	4	$KClO_4$	30
Al-Mg	26-34	Red gum	6	Sb_2S_3	14
CuO	5-11	Dextrine	2.5	Starch	11
S	5-11	C	3	Wood dust	5

Other special effects are the subjects of individual chapters in which they are discussed in detail.

SURVEY OF SOME POPULAR FIREWORKS

The following sections cover the chemistry and manufacturing techniques of some popular fireworks items. More details on these and others can be found in several excellent books[2,6,7,8,9].

Sparklers

Wire sparklers are traditionally available in three colors: gold, red, and green. In red and green sparklers, a $KClO_4$-Al reaction produces the heat, $Ba(NO_3)_2$ adds the green color, and $SrCO_3$ adds the red. The flying sparks are silver or white and are produced by Al metal. Sparkler compositions are similar to those used in many small ground fountains and torches that also glow red or green and emit a shower of sparks.

In the gold sparkler, a $Ba(NO_3)_2$-Al reaction produces heat which causes Fe filings to combust with a characteristic golden color. The slight gas pressure generated in the heated mix ejects the glowing filings as sparks. The sparks cool quickly and produce little or no heat sensation if allowed to strike your hand.

The steel wire commonly used in sparklers serves the important function of heat conductor, promoting the smooth propagation of the pyrotechnic reaction along the sparkler. Attempts to use substitutes for metal wire have had little success.

In manufacture, the pyrotechnic mix is prepared as a slurry, thickened by a binder such as dextrine, and the wires are dipped into the wet mix, usually several times, to pick up the desired thin coating. Fe in a mix is often given a light wax precoat to minimize corrosion in the wet slurry.

A frequent problem with gold sparklers is the tendency for the $Ba(NO_3)_2$, Fe, and Al to react in the wet slurry, e.g., as:

$$36H_2O + 16Al + 3Ba(NO_3)_2 \rightarrow 3Ba(OH)_2 + 16Al(OH)_3 + 6NH_3$$

This decomposition evolves heat which accelerates the reaction and is detectable by its ammonia smell. Sparklers made from a mix that has begun to decompose have inferior quality. The solution reaction can be greatly accelerated by addition of NaOH (a 5% addition to the slurry will cause decomposition within 15 minutes), and can also be effectively controlled by maintenance of suitable pH with additions of a weak acid such as H_3BO_3. A strong acid would attack the Al and Fe filings in the mix.

Sparkler drying also requires care. Moisture must be allowed to evaporate as quickly as possible, yet drying must not be rushed. Too rapid drying forms a surface crust, trapping internal moisture which can cause decomposition and rust.

The gold sparkler is an especially delicate creature and one of the most difficult pyrotechnic devices to make well. If any of the materials are slightly off-standard, or the proportions are incorrect, the sparkler will not perform properly; and if processing variables are not rigorously controlled, e.g., if drying is too fast or the storage atmosphere is too moist, the product will be inferior.

Fountains and Torches

Fountains and torches are ground fireworks that cast a shower of color and sparks which is especially dramatic at night. Like sparklers, they usually contain either Al, for silver or white sparks, or Fe filings or charcoal, for gold sparks.

The pyrotechnic mix is packed in tubes or cones sealed at the bottom with a plug or disc. Walls must be thick enough to resist rupture by internal pressure and plugs or discs must be securely attached. Fountains often have a narrowed aperture (choke) at the top to build up higher pressure and thus spew the sparks to a greater height. However, some U.S. localities have set 12 feet as a maximum height for such fireworks, and fountains sold in these areas are usually not choked.

Roman Candles

A crucial part of the Roman Candle is its tubular casing. To prevent blowing or burning out of the side wall, the tube is strongly constructed of high quality chipboard, convolute rather than spiral wound, and bonded with a heavy flour-and-water paste. Although spiral winding could probably be made strong enough, no U.S. manufacturer uses it for candles.

Tube rolling is an art that is probably as old as the fireworks industry and has elements that may not be obvious. The flour-and-water paste (preserved against biological deterioration by such substances as $HgCl_2$ and phenol) is a good combination because it increases fire resistance. Tubes must be wound and dried so that they remain straight. The camber, or bow, must not exceed 1/8 inch per foot of axial length. The edge of the chipboard strip that becomes part of the inside surface of the tube must be feathered or deckled before rolling so that the interior is almost perfectly round and smooth. Also, the chipboard must be cut and rolled so that the axis of the tube is parallel to the grain of the paper.

A roman candle loading machine is made of four steel uprights which serve as guides and support for a rack of free-mounted rams. Empty tubes are placed into position on studs and aligned with a floating frame in such a way as to allow a perforated funnel collar to be placed on the top ends of the tubes. A shuttleboard (See Chapter XV) is charged with kerosene-moistened clay and positioned over the collar. The charges are dumped and the rams are lowered and bumped to consolidate the clay. Black-powder charges (3F) and then stars are dropped with other shuttleboards. The multiple rams are lowered slowly to gently push the stars to the bottom. Candle-mix charges are then dropped with yet another board and consolidated with bumping. Loading stops when the last charge of candle mix is placed and pressed. It is important that the candle mix be granulated to allow more accurate filling and more uniform compression, which prevent emission of double stars. Figure 1 shows a 6-star candle.

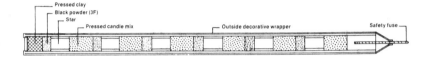

Figure 1. *Roman candle loaded with six stars.*

Rockets with Sticks

Rockets are made with tubes similar to those used in candles. Since the rocket tubes are much shorter than candles, the camber requirement is less stringent.

Rocket tubes (motors) are gang loaded with a hydraulic press. The tubes are slipped onto polished steel mandrels mounted on a plate, and a compound collar-plate with funnel-shaped holes is positioned over the tops of the empty tubes. A measured charge of dampened clay is dropped by means of a shuttleboard. Hollow rams attached to a plate are inserted into the tubes and around the mandrels, and the press is actuated to compact the clay. The ram-plate is removed, a charge of rocket mix is measured into the tubes, the rams are returned, the rocket mix is compressed at about 400 lb dead load, and the rams are again removed. The next increment of rocket mix is compressed with shorter hollow rams having a smaller inside diameter, and the ram length and diameter decrease with each additional charge. The last increment of rocket mix is pressed with solid rams.

The rocket mix is a modified black powder containing somewhat less KNO_3 and S and more charcoal than the conventional powder. Performance depends strongly on the KNO_3 particle size and on the particle size and origin of the charcoal. Compositions usually burn faster if the charcoal is made from soft rather than hard wood.

The loaded motors are decorated with an outside wrapper cut to two inches of extra length which are twisted to form the fuse holder. The top end of the rocket motor is rolled in a dextrine-water mix and glued into a cone (see Figure 2) which serves as a wind shield and a container for the pyrotechnic-display composition.

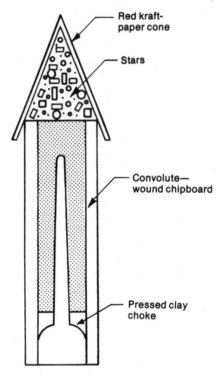

Figure 2. *Cross section of rocket motor and payload.*

The stick—glued, stapled, or wired to the outside of the tube, parallel to the axis—should be two to three times the length of the rocket motor. It should also be heavy enough so that if the assembly is balanced on a knife edge placed under the stick about an inch from the motor, it will tilt toward the stick end.

Firecrackers

Probably the most popular, and certainly one of the most controversial, common fireworks is the small firecracker. Years ago, its length ranged up to over 6 inches and its charge up to several grams of explosive. Misuse of the larger firecrackers caused many serious accidents and injuries and led to their being banned in many localities. In 1966, the federal government limited fire-cracker-type devices to 130 mg of powder, and in 1976, the Consumer Product Safety Commission reduced the limit further to 50 mg, taking virtually all the *bang* out of backyard 4th-of-July celebrations, but also significantly reducing the number and severity of injuries. The 50-mg firecracker has been known to explode in or near a person's hand without causing serious harm.

The firecracker and related devices such as the cherry bomb, silver salute, and M80 (military rifle-fire simulator) are perhaps the easiest fireworks to make, much easier than sparklers and fountains. They require only explosive powder, a paper or cardboard tube, end plugs, and a fuse. Because fire-crackers are so popular and easy to make, a bootleg industry still supplies the banned larger items which take their annual toll in serious injuries. Federal regulations specify severe penalties for violators and both the CPSC and the Bureau of Alcohol, Tobacco and Firearms actively pursue illegal fireworks producers and distributors.

These small explosives are made with various compositions. Black powder itself creates considerable noise, but flash-and-sound mixes containing Al or Mg give a sharper report and a bright flash of light. The familiar 1½-inch Chinese firecracker usually contains a flash-and-sound mix containing $KClO_3$, S, and Al. However, American manufacturers tend toward the less sensitive $KClO_4$ blended with Al and either S or Sb_2S_3.

All of these mixes are extremely hazardous and should be handled only by pyrotechnic experts because they can mass explode during manufacture. Static electricity or any other spark source can set them off. Far too many at-tempts to homemake firecrackers have ended in tragedy. Even in finished items, flash-and-sound powders pose a hazard if amounts exceed a few grains per piece, and a mass explosion is always possible during shipment or storage of bulk quantities. Flash-and-sound mixes are also among the most sensitive to moisture and must be kept dry to prevent spontaneous combustion and ex-plosion.

The type of Al used is the key to making a firecracker produce a satisfyingly loud report. Dark *pyro* Al is clearly the best because of its relatively large surface area and high reactivity. Spherical, *atomized* Al with a reduced surface area per gram of powder is much less effective for pyrotechnics. Al samples should always be tested before use to make sure they will give the desired effect.

Wheels

Rockets and aerial shells are spectacular, but require a large open area for safe use. Devices such as wheels and spinners that move on the ground are alternative means for displaying pyrotechnically generated motion in a confined area. Wheels commonly consist of a cardboard or wooden frame, nailed or otherwise attached to a tree or pole at a center pivot, with two to four drivers mounted on the periphery.

The drivers are heavy cardboard tubes, charged with various mixtures of meal powder and KNO_3-S-charcoal blends, and choked to produce a high thrust. Propelled by high-pressure gas escaping from a driver, the wheel spins furiously about its pivot point, frequently accompanied by sparks, color, or whistling noises. When the composition in one driver is exhausted, an interconnecting fuse transfers the fire to the next, restarting the rotation until all the drivers have been fired. The manufacturer's principal concern is that all drivers and other components be securely attached to the body of the wheel so that pieces do not come loose and fly off.

Wheels range in size from small common-fireworks backyard types to large and elaborate constructions used in public displays. These give the manufacturer the opportunity to express artistry in combining colors and other effects with motion.

Ground spinners are new to the United States, having been introduced by the Chinese in the early 1970s. Their principle is similar to that of the wheel. They are common fireworks devices consisting of one tube, resembling a wheel driver, with its fuse inserted into the side near one end. When ignited, the tube spins rapidly on the ground, emitting color and sparks in a novel and attractive display. One of the most popular spinners is called the *Ground Bloom Flower.*

Special Aerial Shells

A favorite fireworks item is the whistling aerial star shell which combines visual and auditory appeal. The effect is achievable in two ways. In one, shown in Figure 3, the shell whistles while ascending since the column of whistle mix is the first material to ignite as the shell is ejected from the mortar.

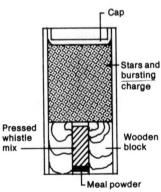

Figure 3. *Aerial shell with ascending whistle.*

The second way is to cap the shell at both ends and simply load the cavity in between with stars and whistles. This construction requires a small length of fireworks fuse glued in the bottom cap to relay ignition from the lifting charge. Sound and light are then produced together in the sky when the fuse burns to the mixed charge.

SAFETY

Like any pyrotechnics or explosives, fireworks and fireworks compositions require expertise and care in manufacture and caution in transportation, storage, and use. The fireworks industry has acted to help educate manufacturers and consumers in proper practices.

A joint effort of the fireworks industry and the Sectional Committee on Explosives of the National Fire Protection Association developed NFPA Code 44A covering the manufacture, transport, and storage of special and common fireworks[10]. The code's philosophy is not "There shall be no accidents." Rather, it advocates that everything humanly possible should be done to prevent accidents, but takes the realistic approach that accidents will happen, that plant design should be based on this assumption, and that plant construction should minimize accidental harm, especially to personnel.

Another feature of Code 44A is its recognition that explosives and the more general run of pyrotechnics pose different hazards and require different safety measures. With an explosive, the goal is containment of the blast with heavy barricades. With pyrotechnics, confinement accelerates the decomposition reaction, promotes pressure buildup, and increases the risk of explosion and scattering of burning fragments.

A fireworks building should provide pressure relief by incorporating an intentionally weak wall or roof that will yield to mild pressure, venting the building in case of fire and preventing escalation to an explosion. Screen-type barricades are highly recommended around potential *donor* buildings to minimize the escape of flying fragments and to reduce the probability that a fire will spread to nearby buildings.

NFPA Code 1123, a cooperative product of the fireworks industry and the NFPA Committee on Pyrotechnics, covers procedures for site selection and for safely managing a public fireworks display. It contains valuable information for public safety officials who bear the responsibility for supervising such displays.

Finally, to help minimize injuries from the use of common fireworks, the industry and the Consumer Product Safety Commission developed rigid standards for construction, chemical composition, fusing, and labeling[4]. The industry also sponsors an annual educational program just before the 4th of July in which it stresses safety tips for fireworks use by the public and strongly discourages the use of illegal, large firecracker-type explosives and attempts to construct homemade fireworks.

When the fireworks industry consisted of a fragmented group of small manufacturing and distributing companies, it was able to contribute only in a minor way to public education in the safe use of fireworks. Since the founding of the American Pyrotechnics Association in 1948, the industry has developed an effective organization that works responsibly with government agencies and the NFPA to promote public safety.

NEW DIRECTIONS

Traditionally, fireworks have changed very slowly. Formulas have been handed down from grandfather to father to son without alteration. An example of this is the continuing almost exclusive use of natural thickeners and binders such as dextrine, wheat paste, and red gum in spite of the availability of possibly superior synthetics. The time is now ripe for advances that may come more rapidly than in the past. These may be expected in several areas.

Although new synthetic polymers, such as polyvinylchloride (PVC) and the epoxies, have had little impact on the fireworks industry, they are now competitive in cost so that their more reproducible characteristics have greater appeal. They are also less prone to ferment or otherwise decompose and will undoubtedly be used more and more. PVC is a particularly attractive binder because it donates chlorine, which enhances color, and is now used in some Chinese fireworks.

The use of metal coatings such as PVC and various waxes to retard corrosion should become widespread. Dipping metal powder in coatings dissolved in volatile organic solvent and allowing the solvent to evaporate leaves a thin protective layer on the particles which should lengthen shelf life.

Innovations can be expected in the wire sparkler in the form of multicolors and a coating on the tip (especially of the 20- and 36-inch sparklers) to make ignition easier. Another multicolor advance that has eluded production efforts for years may finally become a commercial possibility—a red, white, and blue torch. Attempts have failed so far because combustion of the red and white composition builds up a chimney of pyrotechnic residue that inhibits the blue, a color that is difficult to produce under ideal conditions. If a volatile red and white composition can be found, the blue could shine through.

> And the rockets' red glare
> The bombs bursting in air
> Gave proof through the night
> That our flag was still there.
> Francis Scott Key, 1814

Chapter XI

REFERENCES

1. *U.S. Federal Register,* June 8, 1976, p. 22923 and *U.S. Code of Federal Regulations* Title 16, Chapter II, Subchapter C, parts 1500 and 1507.

2. Lancaster, R., Shimizu, T., Butler, R.E.A., and Hall, R.G., *Fireworks Principles and Practice,* Chemical Publishing Co., New York, 1972.

3. DOT Class C: *U.S. Code of Federal Regulations,* Title 49, part 173.100 (r).

4. Conkling, J.A., *New Federal Standards for Class C Fireworks,* NFPA Fire Journal, May, 1977.

5. National Fire Protection Association NFPA Code 1123, *Public Display of Fireworks,* Boston, 1978.

6. Ellern, H., *Military and Civilian Pyrotechnics,* Chemical Publishing Co., New York, 1968.

7. Shidlovskiy, A.A., *Foundations of Pyrotechnics,* Report FTD-II-63-758 (trans. DDC AD 602 687), Air Force Systems Command, Wright-Patterson AFB, Ohio, 1964.

8. Davis, T.L., *The Chemistry of Powder and Explosives,* Wiley, New York, 1941.

9. Weingart, G.W., *Pyrotechnics,* 2nd ed., Chemical Publishing Co., New York, 1947.

10. National Fire Protection Association NFPA Code 44A, *Code for the Manufacture, Transport, and Storage of Fireworks,* Boston, 1974.

Chapter XII

ANALYSIS OF PYROTECHNIC COMPOSITIONS

I don't care how good old methods are, new methods are better even if they're only just as good.

G. H. Lorimer

The analysis of pyrotechnic compositions can be attacked by a variety of classical and modern instrumental methods. The method to choose for a particular problem depends on the equipment available and the urgency of the results.

DIFFERENTIAL THERMAL ANALYSIS

Early workers in the field of solid-state reactivity used heating-rate studies to determine the onset of a chemical reaction. Hedvall[1] writes, "It was my primary object to investigate if his (Tammann's) thermo-analytical method could be used for determining reaction temperatures in non-metallic powder mixtures. Tammann was dubious, but by choosing suitable substances in the powder mixtures and suitable heating conditions I was soon able to demonstrate that the heating curves exhibited unmistakable jumps at the temperatures where a reaction started."

In the early 1960s, the differential thermal analyzer[2] began to be commercially marketed and became available to many researchers. The instrument works on the same principle as Hedvall's apparatus but is more versatile, sensitive, and accurate.

Differential thermal analysis (DTA) is a technique for detecting the release or absorption of energy that accompanies chemical or physical changes in a sample being heated at a uniform rate. Changes that absorb energy (e.g., melting, boiling, sublimation, some types of decomposition, phase changes, and dehydration) are called endotherms. Changes that release energy are called exotherms.

DTA senses enthalpy changes by comparing the temperature of the test sample with that of an inert reference material which does not undergo changes over the measured temperature range, while both sample and reference are heated identically in a common heating block. A third sensor measures the block's temperature (see Figure 1) which the sample would have if it were not subject to chemical or physical changes. The block temperature is essentially that of the reference and is programmed to rise at an approximately linear rate.

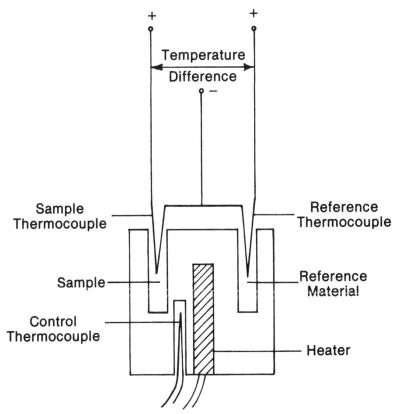

Figure 1. *Schematic of basic differential thermal analysis apparatus.*

When an endotherm occurs, the test sample temperature temporarily drops below that of the reference (which experiences no endotherm) so a negative difference is measured. Conversely, an exotherm temporarily raises the test-sample temperature. The temperature difference between sample and reference is recorded as a function of the block (nominal sample) temperature, and dips and rises trace a characteristic signature of the substance or mix.

DTA can be valuable for pyrotechnic studies in a number of ways. First, mixes can be qualitatively analyzed from an examination of the endotherms in the preignition temperature range of the thermogram (DTA record). For example, KNO_3 (melting point 334 °C) shows a sharp endotherm at about 130 °C, corresponding to a rhombic-trigonal crystal transition. $KClO_4$ (melting point 610 °C) displays an endotherm at about 300 °C corresponding to a rhombic-cubic transition. The presence of S in a mix usually reveals itself by endotherms at 105 °C (rhombic-monoclinic transition) and at about 120 °C (melting). $KClO_3$, on the other hand, undergoes no solid-solid transitions in the 20 °C to 350 °C region until it melts at 356 °C. Figures 2 through 9 show representative DTA thermograms.

DTA can also determine ignition temperatures of pyrotechnic mixes rapidly heated in a glass capillary tube. Such studies can indicate the sensitivity of the mixes to being activated by heat and help to predict storage stability.

Finally, DTA gives a rapid indication of relative purity. Since impurities greatly influence melting points, a sharp endotherm at the generally accepted melting temperature supports a presumption of reasonable purity. A broad endothermic pattern peaking below the expected melting point is associated with impurities and suggests caution in the use of the contaminated material.

Figures 2-9. DTA *thermograms.*

(Vertical scale indicates temperature difference)

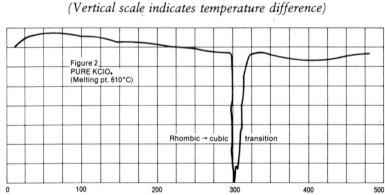

Temperature, °C

DTA *thermograms (continued)*

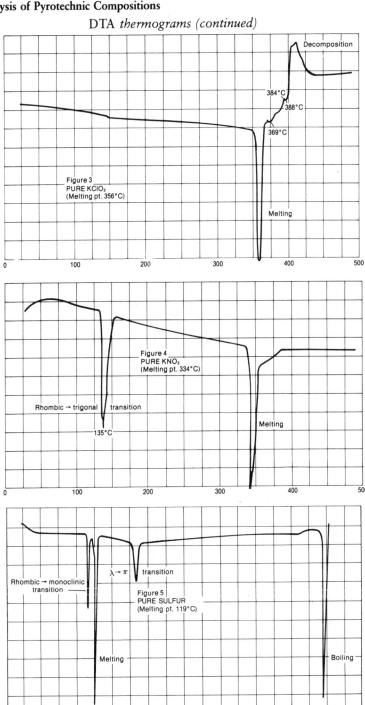

Decomposition

384°C
388°C
369°C

Figure 3
PURE KClO₃
(Melting pt. 356°C)

Melting

0   100   200   300   400   500

Figure 4
PURE KNO₃
(Melting pt. 334°C)

Rhombic → trigonal   transition

Melting

135°C

0   100   200   300   400   500

λ → π   transition

Rhombic → monoclinic
transition ———

Figure 5
PURE SULFUR
(Melting pt. 119°C)

Melting

Boiling

0   100   200   300   400   500

Temperature, °C

DTA *thermograms (continued)*

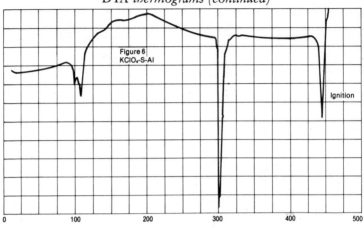

Figure 6
KClO₄-S-Al

Ignition

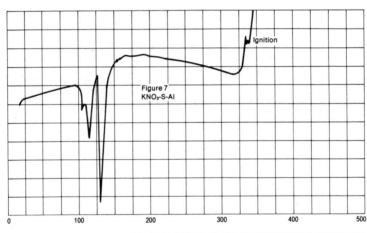

Ignition

Figure 7
KNO₃-S-Al

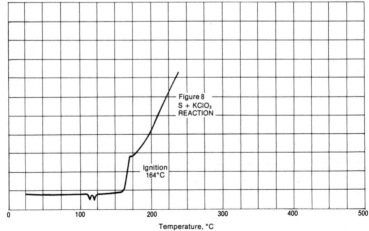

Figure 8
S + KClO₃
REACTION

Ignition
164°C

Temperature, °C

DTA Thermograms (continued)

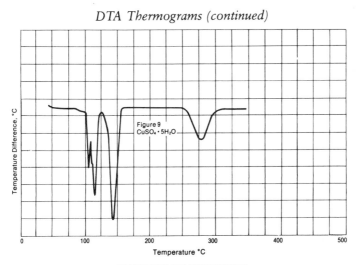

THERMOGRAVIMETRY

Another thermal analytic technique applicable to pyrotechnics is thermogravimetry[2], the use of a sensitive balance to measure the increase or decrease in sample mass as a function of temperature. Evolution of gaseous products (e.g., in the decomposition of $KClO_3$ or the dehydration of $CuSO_4 \cdot 5H_2O$) causes a weight loss, while reactions such as the air oxidation of Mg metal cause a weight increase.

Usually, heat is added at a rate that raises the sample temperature linearly with time, but the method is also used to monitor mass change versus time at a constant temperature. Figure 10 shows the thermogravimetric (TG) curve for the dehydration of $CuSO_4 \cdot 5H_2O$.

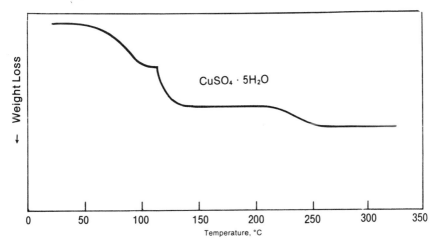

Figure 10. *Thermogravimetric curve for dehydration of* $CuSO_4 \cdot 5H_2O$.

INFRARED SPECTROSCOPY

Compounds have molecular rotational and vibrational energy levels associated with the binding forces holding the constituent parts together. When excited by arc or spark, the compound will emit characteristic infrared radiation corresponding to transitions among these energy levels. Conversely, if irradiated with infrared rays, the compound will preferentially absorb energy at these same wavelengths. Infrared spectroscopy[3] measures the emission or absorption pattern and helps to identify the unknown material. Figures 11 through 16 show typical spectrometer traces. Table IV contains infrared data for some common pyrotechnic oxidizers[4]. Infrared spectroscopy of these oxidizers promises to be a valuable complement to DTA for the qualitative and quantitative analysis of pyrotechnic mixes.

Figures 11 - 16. *Infrared spectra.*
(Vertical scale indicates % transmittance)

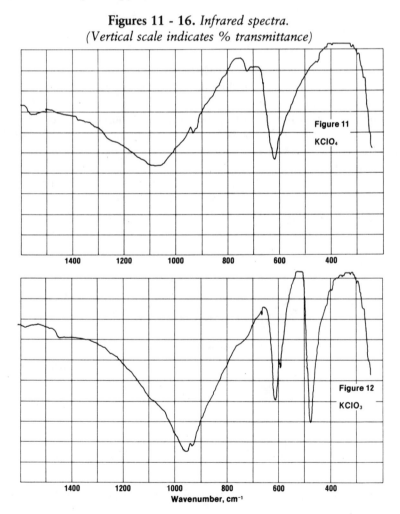

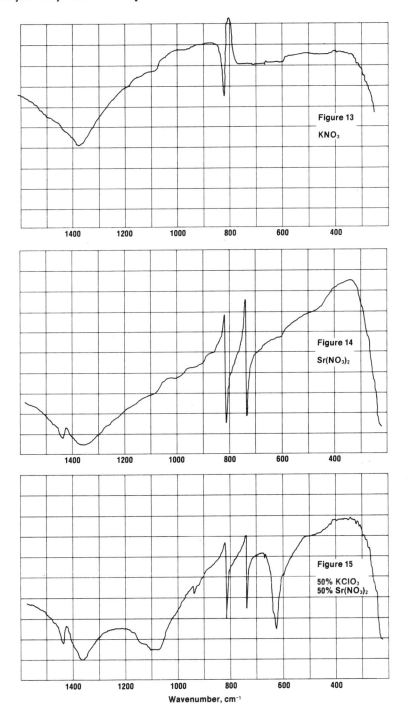

Figure 13
KNO_3

Figure 14
$Sr(NO_3)_2$

Figure 15
50% $KClO_3$
50% $Sr(NO_3)_2$

Wavenumber, cm⁻¹

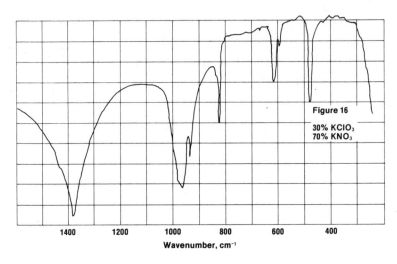

Figure 16
30% KClO₃
70% KNO₃

Wavenumber, cm⁻¹

Table IV. Characteristic infrared peaks for common oxidizers

Oxidizer	Wavenumber, cm^{-1}
$KClO_3$	1900, 960, 935, 615, 478
$KClO_4$	1075(broad), 935(weak), 620
NH_4ClO_4	1070(broad), 930(weak), 620
KNO_3	1760(weak), 1375(broad), 825
$NaNO_3$	1785, 1370(broad), 830, 725(weak)
NH_4NO_3	1760(weak), 1375(broad), 820, 715
$Sr(NO_3)_2$	1790, 1370(broad), 815, 735
$Ba(NO_3)_2$	1775, 1350(broad), 815, 730

THERMAL CONDUCTIMETRIC ANALYSIS

Solid-state chemists have long relied on electrical conductivity studies to determine the temperature required to initiate reactions, e.g., in the BaO-AgI system. AgI goes through a solid-solid transition from yellow hexagonal to orange cubic in the 138 °C to 150 °C temperature region. As seen in Figure 17, a sharp rise in electrical conductivity indicates the onset of mobility in the lattice. The reaction rate of $BaO + 2AgI \rightarrow Ag_2O + BaI_2$ also peaks in this lattice interval.

Conductivity measurements are especially revealing for the reactions:

$$3BaO_2 + 2Fe \rightarrow Fe_2O_3 + 3BaO$$

$$2PbO + Si \rightarrow SiO_2 + 2Pb$$

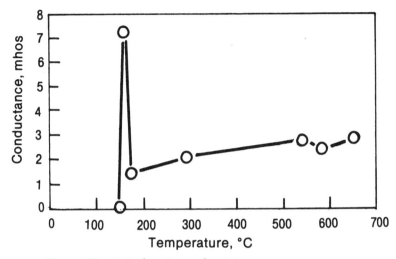

Figure 17. AgI *electric conductivity vs temperature.*

Figure 18 shows data for two sample pellets of each type. In the first reaction, conductivity starts high because of the presence of Fe metal and falls

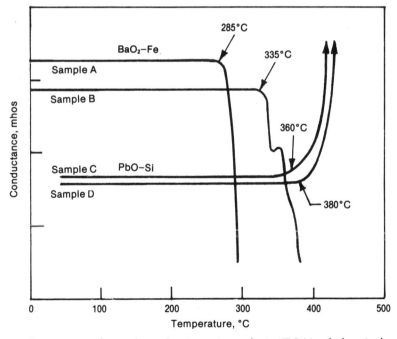

Figure 18. *Thermal conductimetric analysis* (TCA) *of chemical reactions that cause switching of electric conductivity*[5].

sharply as the reaction produces only insulating oxides. In the second reaction, the initial conductivity is relatively low because the free Si is a semiconductor not a conductor. However, the reaction product, Pb, is a true metallic conductor so the conductivity rises at the onset of the reaction. Differences between two curves for the same reaction indicate differences between pellet samples. The conductivity measurements permit a study of both the onset temperature and extent of the reaction. Apparatus used for the measurements is shown in Figure 19 and was later modified as described in McLain and McClure[5].

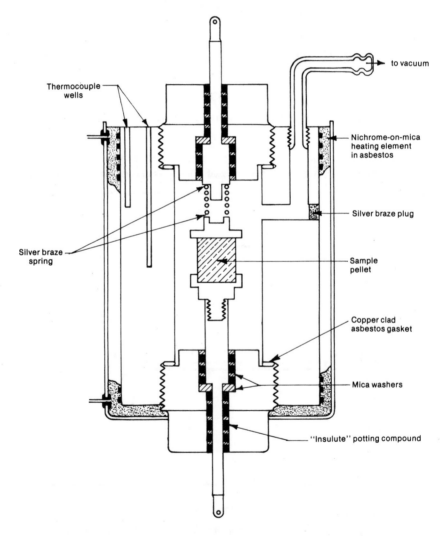

Figure 19. *Test cell for thermal conductimetric analysis of sample pellets[5].*

Use of this conductivity cell for thermal analysis was first believed to be unique, but Jen Chiu[6] reported in 1965 that he had pursued a parallel path. Apparently, neither Chiu nor Berg and Burmistrova[7] used pellet samples at that time, but Chiu has recently stated that he has been using them for some time. The Chiu cell is not yet commercially available, but a description has been published[8], as has a technique for simultaneous thermogravimetric, derivative thermogravimetric, differential thermal, and electrothermal (ETA) analysis[9].

ELECTROTHERMAL ANALYSIS

ETA consists of the measurement of the variation of capacitance (or dielectric constant) and the dissipation factor (or loss tangent) with temperature, as opposed to the TCA measurement of conductivity. Capacitance is related to the electric polarizability of a crystal which increases when the restraining forces are weakened during a transition between two stable crystal forms. The dissipation factor is a measure of heat lost from an imposed AC test signal and also rises during a crystal transition. Figure 20 shows an ETA graph for a standard sample of KNO_3. A transition is evident below 0 °C, but of greater significance for pyrotechnics is the crystal transition representing the onset of nitrate spin at 129 °C, which agrees well with the DTA value of 130 °C and the thermodynamic value of 127.7 °C.

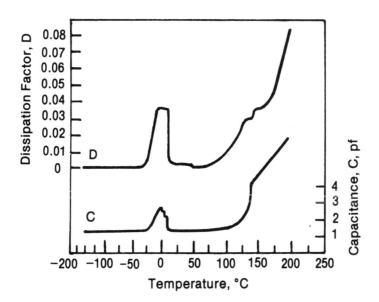

Figure 20. *Electrothermal analysis* (ETA) *of* KNO_3[8].

CLASSICAL CHEMICAL ANALYSIS

A rapid qualitative analysis of a pyrotechnic composition is sometimes needed which may or may not be followed by quantitative analysis. Special instruments may not be on hand. For example, the tests may determine if a composition complies with the U.S. Department of Transportation ban on shipment of mixtures containing both ammonium and chlorate salts, or the U.S. Consumer Product Safety Commission restrictions on $KClO_3$, Mg, and other toxic or highly reactive chemicals in common fireworks. A program has been developed for analyzing the oxidizers and fuels most commonly used in fireworks, similar to the method first proposed by Weingart[10], which can also be modified for testing other materials where appropriate.

Positive ions

The analytic method[11] consists of first adding 300 mg of the mix under test to 8 to 10 ml of distilled water, stirring well to ensure solution of all water-soluble constituents, and filtering the slurry to separate solution and residue. Add one drop of saturated Na_2SO_4 solution to a small portion of the filtrate. A white precipitate indicates the presence of Ba^{2+} or Sr^{2+} ions. To distinguish between Ba and Sr, perform the flame test on the remaining untreated filtrate with a platinum wire and a bunsen burner. The flame is green for Ba salts, red for Sr salts. Do the flame test before adding Na_2SO_4 since Na^+ ions in the filtrate will add a yellow flame that masks other colors.

Then add Na_2SO_4 solution to the filtrate drop by drop until no further precipitate forms, and filter out the precipitated sulfate of Ba or Sr. (Their removal is necessary to prepare for later anion tests.) The sulfate precipitate may be dried and weighed to analyze for quantities of Ba or Sr.

Tests for other positive ions require use of the original untreated filtrate. The Na^+ ion may be detectable by a yellow color in the platinum wire flame test. The NH_4^+ ion makes its presence known by an ammonia smell after the test filtrate is made alkaline with NaOH solution.

The K^+ ion is difficult to detect because its violet flame is easily masked by other colors and most of its compounds are water soluble. If DTA apparatus is available, KNO_3 and $KClO_4$ can be identified by their characteristic endotherms. The best method is probably atomic absorption spectroscopy, if equipment is accessible, which can also give quantitative data.

Oxidizing anions-Qualitative

Tests for oxidizing anions are performed on the filtrate from which Ba^{2+} and Sr^{2+} ions have been removed.

ClO_3^-: Prepare a reagent by adding 20 g aniline hydrochloride to 50 ml concentrated HCl[12]. Stir briefly. The reagent will remain usable for months if stored in a tightly stoppered bottle. For the test, add about 1 ml of reagent to 1 ml of the filtrate. As little as 1% $KClO_3$ by weight in the mix being examined will turn the solution pink, then violet, and finally dark blue. Nitrates and perchlorates will not color the solution. The aniline hydrochloride test for ClO_3^- is more reliable and safer than the Weingart test[10], which requires adding a drop of concentrated H_2SO_4 to the dry test mix. If ClO_3^- is present, the H_2SO_4 will usually cause the mix to burst into flames.

NO_3^-: Prepare the reagent by dissolving 25 g $FeSO_4$ in 100 ml distilled water and add 25 ml concentrated H_2SO_4[13]. Store in a tightly stoppered glass bottle and replace with new reagent when a yellowish color develops. To test for NO_3^-, add 2 ml of reagent (4 ml if the previous test for ClO_3^- was positive) to 2 ml of the original filtrate solution, and mix by shaking or stirring. Then tilt the test tube slightly and allow an addition of 1 ml of concentrated H_2SO_4 to slide down the tube wall into the solution. The denser H_2SO_4 will sink to the bottom. The presence of NO_3^- will cause a brown or purple-brown ring to form immediately at the interface between the water and the H_2SO_4. Neither ClO_3^- nor ClO_4^- will produce colored rings under these conditions.

ClO_4^-: Prepare Zwikker's reagent by mixing 40 ml 10% aqueous $CuSO_4$ solution, 19 ml pyridine, and 50 ml distilled water[14]. Avoid breathing the pyridine vapor. Store the deep-blue reagent in a tightly stoppered glass bottle. For the test, add 2 ml of Zwikker's reagent to approximately 3 ml of the test filtrate. If a precipitate does not form immediately, vigorously scratch the bottom of the test tube with a glass rod to induce crystallization. The precipitation of blue or violet crystals of $Cu(C_5H_5N)_4(ClO_4)_2$ (cupric pyridine perchlorate) indicates the presence of ClO_4^-. Neither NO_3^- nor ClO_3^- will cause precipitation under these conditions, nor will they interfere with the test for ClO_4^-. The test is conclusive since no precipitate will form if ClO_4^- is absent.

Oxidizing Anions - Quantitative[15]
ClO_3^-: Convert ClO_3^- to Cl^- by adding excess $NaHSO_3$ solution to a volume of filtrate that corresponds to a known weight of the pyrotechnic mix under test. Then precipitate AgCl by adding excess $AgNO_3$ solution, filter, and weigh the precipitate. One gram of AgCl corresponds to 0.855 g $KClO_3$ in the mix. NO_3^- and ClO_4^- do not interfere with this analysis.

ClO_4^-: A tetraphenylphosphonium chloride solution used as a reagent permits quantitative analysis for ClO_4^- in the form of the tetraphenylphosphonium salt[16] without interference by ClO_3^- or NO_3^- ions.

NO_3^-: After first removing all ClO_3^- and ClO_4^- from the solution, use nitron to precipitate NO_3^- for quantitative determination[17].

Metals, sulfur, and charcoal

Metals, sulfur, and charcoal are the most likely materials to be found in the water-insoluble portions of the test mix. Mg will cause visible evolution of H_2 bubbles on addition of 5% acetic acid, whereas Al will not. Al will cause H_2 bubbling if the addition is 5% HCl or 5% NaOH solution. Fe dissolves in dilute HCl or HNO_3 and will produce a Prussian Blue color when a few drops of potassium ferrocyanide solution are added to the acid. Because S dissolves in CS_2 and in pyridine, it can be extracted from other solids and leaves a characteristic yellow residue after the solvents evaporate. Charcoal is insoluble in acids, CS_2, and water, survives as a black residue, and colors a bunsen burner flame orange.

Organic binders and fuels

Organic binders, such as dextrine, red gum, wheat paste, and PVC, are difficult to analyze quickly by solution methods because their solubilities vary widely. Sugars dissolve easily in water. PVC is almost insoluble. Infrared spectroscopy is the best analytic technique for these materials, centered about the 3000-cm^{-1} region corresponding to stretching of the C-H bond, in addition to the characteristic infrared spectrum for the particular substance under investigation.

ENTROPY OF TRANSITION - MODIFIED TROUTON'S RULE

The previous discussion of the relation between conductivity changes and crystal transitions, particularly the AgI hexagonal-to-cubic phase change (an outstanding example of the Hedvall Effect), brings to mind Trouton's Rule for liquids. In 1884, F. Trouton stated that the entropy of vaporization of normal liquids is a constant:

$$\Delta S_V = \Delta H_V / T_b = 21 \text{ entropy units}$$

where ΔS_V is the entropy change at vaporization, ΔH_V is the enthalpy change at vaporization, and T_b is the boiling point in degrees Kelvin.

This was based on the assumption that all liquids near their boiling point have the same degree of randomness, and that molecules of a gas have attained the ultimate degree of randomness. Consequently, the difference in entropy between the gas and the liquid should be a constant.

Like most generalizations, Trouton's Rule has been noted more for exceptions than for exactness. For example, hydrogen bonding in liquids such as water, methanol, and ethanol creates a certain degree of structure, hence a lower entropy, even at their boiling points, than is found in liquids that lack hydrogen bonding. The difference in entropy between the gas and the hydrogen-bonded liquids is therefore greater (about 26 entropy units) than predicted by Trouton's Rule. Conversely, hydrogen bonding causes acetic acid to exist as dimers in its early vapor state, a degree of order that reduces the gas entropy. The difference in entropy between the gas and the liquid is therefore smaller (about 15 entropy units) than the Trouton constant.

These considerations may be usefully applied to solid-solid phase transitions. If the heats of transition can be measured, e.g., in the transformation of AgI from hexagonal to cubic, or S from rhombic to monoclinic, and characteristic entropy changes can be assigned to each transition, then DTA records for transition temperatures can be used to determine crystal classes.

Each is given a bag of tools,
A shapeless mass,
A book of rules;
And each must make,
Ere life has flown
A stumbling block
Or a stepping stone.

R. L. Sharpe

Chapter XII

REFERENCES

1. Hedvall, J.A., *Solid State Chemistry, Whence, Where and Whither,* Elsevier, London, 1966; p. 5.
2. Wendlandt, W.W., *Thermal Methods of Analysis,* 2nd ed., Wiley, New York, 1974.
3. Bellamy, L.J., *The Infrared Spectra of Complex Molecules,* Wiley, New York, 1958.
4. Voorstad, P.J. and Conkling, J.A., Senior Thesis, Washington College, Chestertown, Md., 1979.
5. McLain, J.H. and McClure, M.D., *Effects of Phase Change in Solid-Solid Reactions,* Final Report, Grant DA-AMC-18-035-77(A), Chemical Research Laboratories, Edgewood Arsenal, Md., 1968.
6. Chiu, J., "A New Approach to Electrical Thermal Analysis," presented at 4th Annual Thermal Analysis Institute of the American Chemical Society, June 21, 1965.
7. Berg, L.G. and Burmistrova, N.P., *Russian J. Inorg. Chem.* **5**, 326 (1960).
8. Chiu, J., *Thermochimica Acta* **8**, 15-25 (1974).
9. Chiu, J., *Anal. Chem.* **39**, 861-867 (1967).
10. Weingart, G.W., *Pyrotechnics,* 2nd ed., Chemical Publishing Co., New York, 1947; p. 220.
11. Suskin, M. and Conkling, J.A., *Rapid Qualitative Analysis of Pyrotechnic Compositions,* presented at Annual Meeting of the Pyrotechnics and Explosives Applications Section, American Defense Preparedness Association, Sunnyvale, Cal., 1976.
12. Fresenius, T.W., *Introduction to Qualitative Chemical Analysis,* 17th ed., Wiley, New York, 1921; p. 492.
13. Smith, W.T., *Laboratory Manual for College Chemistry,* 4th ed., Harper and Row, New York, 1976; p. 248.
14. Shead, A.C. and Bailey, P.W., *Mikrochemie* **33**, 1 (1947).
15. Devan, T.N. and Conkling, J.A., Senior Thesis, Washington College, Chestertown, Md., 1977.
16. Willard, H.H. and Perkins, L.R., *Anal. Chem.* **25**, 1634 (1953).
17. Welcher, F.J., *Organic Analytical Reagents,* Van Nostrand, New York, 1947; Vol. III, Chapter III, pp. 64-104.

Chapter XIII

IGNITION

The beginning is the most important part of the work.

Plato

The usual approach to the solution of pyrotechnic and propellant ignition problems has been largely empirical. The designer specifies what seems like enough material to do the job at ordinary temperatures, then adds more for good measure to ensure performance at $-65\,°F$. Other requirements must also be considered. Perhaps the igniter must produce a slag rather than a gas, or vice versa. Sometimes ignition must be fast, other times slow. The application may call for impinging incandescent particles or only a quick flash of flame.

Unfortunately, igniters designed empirically are too often undependable. They may sometimes underignite and cause propagation failures, or overignite and cause an explosion or a burning path that bypasses a delay train. If an ignition source is borderline in effectiveness, increasing the quantity may entail unexpected scale-up problems. Igniter design is therefore both important and complex. One aspect of the complexity is nomenclature. Igniters are variously called starter mix, first fire, priming mix, igniters, primers, squibs, torches, and igniting fuses or fuzes.

PROBLEMS AND EXAMPLES

Jet aircraft starter cartridges

Propellant in hollow cylinders is ignited to generate gas pressure that rotates the engine's turbine blades. Igniter performance is represented by pressure-time curves as shown in Figure 1. Specifications include the operating and peak pressures, the time to reach operating pressure, the minimum time at the desired pressure, and the total area under the curve. A typical problem may consist of the generation of excessively high peak pressures at 165 °F (dashed upper curve) which can create enough thrust to damage turbine blades, in spite of the igniter grain's meeting all requirements at 77 °F (solid curve). At − 65 °F (lower curve), the pressure may never rise high enough to turn the turbine at all. The solution in this case was the use of three igniter stages each with a modified propellant having a different temperature characteristic.

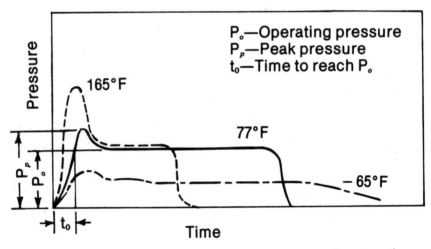

Figure 1. *Problematic pressure-time characteristics of jet aircraft starter cartridge.*

Illuminating-flare igniter

To ignite an illuminating flare mix, a design engineer selected a stab-type primer containing:

40%	basic lead styphnate
20%	lead azide
5%	tetracene
20%	$Ba(NO_3)_2$
15%	Sb_2S_3

The choice was bad because the primer, although sensitive to stab, was also extremely gassy and had a very short-lived flame front. Also aggravating the problem was the fact that the primer fired into a gas-tight enclosure. Consequently, first trials produced blowbacks and blowouts but not ignition. A low-gas composition containing powdered Zr proved more successful.

Flame-thrower igniter

A fast stream of incandescent particles was needed to ignite a rod-like column of napalm-thickened gasoline being ejected at high velocity from a flame thrower. A successful igniter design contained $KClO_4$, sucrose, asphaltum, and both atomized and granular Al, which supplied the necessary heat, gas, and long-burning Al particles. A similar igniter design successfully started a ram-jet engine after modification to yield the higher pressures needed to penetrate the fuel-air stream.

Illuminating-grenade igniter

A first attempt to correct ignition failures of an illuminating grenade consisted of adding black powder. However, this dangerously increased pressure in the grenade. A non-gaseous PbO_2-CuO-Si first fire was an effective and safer substitute for the black powder.

ALTERNATIVE TO EMPIRICAL DESIGN

Recent understanding may help designers to escape from a purely empirical approach to ignition problem solving. This requires distinguishing between ignition temperature and ignition sensitivity.

Ignition temperature

Ignition temperature can be defined as the lowest temperature of the reactants at which the reaction emits enough heat to bring the adjacent reaction zone and surroundings to the same temperature as that of the reactants. Time is important. If the reacting quantity is too small, or if heat travels too slowly to adjacent material, then the fire fails to propagate and goes out. Measurement of ignition temperatures requires not only testing but also data interpretation and understanding of the basic process of ignition.

Henkin and McGill[1] refined the old Wood's-metal bath technique to permit determination of activation energies and other related quantities from which ignition temperatures can be derived. The technique consists of placing 1 g of the substance under test into a brass or copper tube (usually a No. 6 blasting-cap shell), immersing the tube in a Wood's-metal bath heated to a particular temperature T, and timing the interval t before ignition. The bath temperature is then varied and additional samples tested to obtain five or six points through which a temperature-time curve can be drawn as in Figure 2. The assigned ignition temperature is taken to be the one for which ignition occurs within 5 sec. This is 300 °C for the hypothetical substance illustrated in Figure 2. Plotting the Henkin-McGill data in the form of log t vs $1/T$, as in Figure 3, where T is now expressed in degrees Kelvin, yields approximately straight lines from the slopes of which activation energies can be calculated.

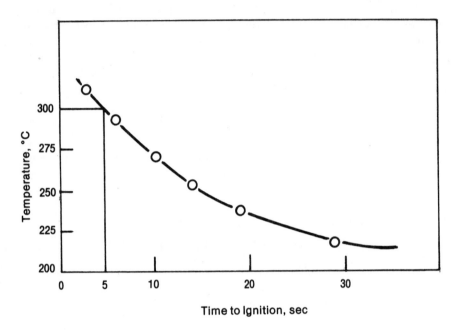

Figure 2. *Ignition time vs mix temperature, Henkin-McGill method.*

The technique has obvious limitations. Results depend on the apparatus used, the pressure, the heating rate, and the homogeneity of the test mix. However, it can give valuable information about a family of mixes that have the same constituents in different proportions. For example, the graphs in Figure 3 represent $KClO_3$-S-$NaHCO_3$ colored smoke-fuel mixes with varied $KClO_3$-S ratios. A and B are two different samples of mixes with the same 2.55:1 ratio, which is stoichiometric. In C, the ratio is 3:1 and in D it is only 2:1. Since the A, B, and C slopes are approximately equal at 8700, while the $KClO_3$-deficient D mix has a slope of 16,700, almost twice the others, it seems clear that the mix is sensitive only to deficiencies of $KClO_3$.

The logarithmic graphs also give other information. Extrapolating the straight lines to a very short time of the order of 0.01 sec determines the temperatures at which ignition occurs almost instantly. This is called the maximum spontaneous ignition temperature, $S.I.T._{max}$. If the graphs are replotted in the form of log $1/t$ vs $1/T°K$ and extrapolated to very long times of the order of 1000 sec, they indicate temperatures at which ignition is delayed for prolonged periods. Such a temperature is called the minimum spontaneous ignition temperature, $S.I.T._{min}$.

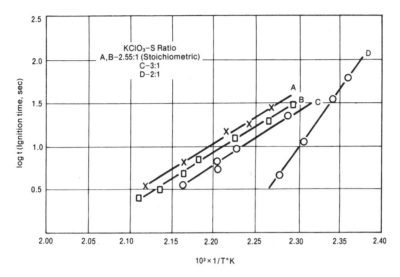

Figure 3. *Logarithmic graph of Henkin-McGill ignition data.*

The physical significance of $S.I.T._{min}$ is fairly clear. It is the temperature at which the P.I.R. starts and is related to long-term storage stability of a mix. It can be characterized as the "onset of exothermicity" and confirmed by DTA tests. For example, graphs for a 70:30 $BaCrO_4$-Mg mix indicated an $S.I.T._{min}$ of 75 °C. Long-term storage in a hot climate of munitions containing this mix as a first fire resulted in ignition failures, and chemical analysis confirmed that most of the Mg had indeed been oxidized.

The physical significance of $S.I.T._{max}$ is less clear, but is certainly related to the mix's flame temperature. Intuitively, one might regard it as the temperature necessary to sustain propagation in a particular configuration. For example, $S.I.T._{max}$ determinations for four different $KClO_3$-S mixes yielded values of 212, 240, 200 and 200 °C, while the $S.I.T._{max}$ for a black-powder mix was 735 °C. This comparison clearly shows that $KClO_3$ is superior to KNO_3 as a low-temperature oxidizer and explains why no adequate substitute has been found for $KClO_3$ in colored smokes, star compositions, insecticide dispersers, and other pyrotechnic applications.

Ignition sensitivity

Ignition sensitivity evokes the concept of ease of ignition. However, since a pyrotechnic composition can be ignited in a variety of ways with different degrees of ease, the establishment of a unique measure of ignition sensitivity requires a careful definition of test conditions. For example, the question arises, "Sensitivity to what - to static spark, impact, friction, primer flash, heat, shock, or some other agent?"

Ignition by these means differs significantly from ignition by heat alone as in the Henkin-McGill tests. In practice, a solid composition is normally ignited by a primer flash or fuse spit, sometimes with the aid of a first-fire relay. No obvious relationship is discernible between such ignition (which triggers the mix to begin its own self-sustained heating and propagation of burning) and Henkin-McGill heating of the whole mass of material to the ignition temperature. Nor does the ignition temperature reveal sensitivity to such influences as friction and impact.

To provide a firm basis for one measure of ignition sensitivity (ease of ignition), McLain and Frahm[2] attempted to generate a short-lived, intermittent spark of reproducible temperature and mass by replacing the needle in a motor-driven sewing machine with an electrically heated incandescent Pt-Ir filament. They pressed test mixes into small primer cups and positioned them so that the filament at the lowest point of its travel approached as closely as possible without touching the surface of the mix. A cigarette paper served as a thickness gauge and shim. A rheostat controlled the filament temperature, indicated indirectly by the voltage and current readings.

With the motor running at a fixed speed, the time spent by the incandescent filament at the surface of the test mix was held constant. The power in watts fed to the filament was then varied until flash occurred. Since black powder was believed to be especially sensitive to primer flash, it was used to calibrate the apparatus. Each test mix was assigned a numerical value for ease of ignition on a scale of 1 through 6 (1 signifies the easiest), based on the filament wattage required to ignite the mix under the test conditions. Table I shows the results for black powder and eight other compositions in comparison with the Henkin-McGill ignition temperatures. No relation appears between the ignition temperatures and the ease of ignition.

Workers at the laboratories of the Bundesanstalt für Material Prufung in Schlebusch, West Germany practice another method of measuring sensitivity to ignition by sparks. They create presumably constant sparks by mechanically turning a steel striker wheel against a lighter flint held to the wheel at constant pressure. The sparks are funneled through a short tube against the surface of the mix under test, and the measure of sensitivity is the maximum distance between spark source and test mix that results in ignition in one of ten trials.

Table I. Ignition sensitivity to hot filament

Mixture	Composition %	Filament watts	Ignition Temperature °C	Ignition Ease 1 (easiest) - 6
Sulfurless meal powder	90 KNO$_3$ 10 charcoal	2.46		1
Red lead starter	90 Pb$_3$O$_4$ 10 Si	2.86	555	2
Red lead starter	54.2 Pb$_3$O$_4$ 34.2 Mn 11.6 Si	2.86	540	2
Litharge silicon	78.4 PbO 19.6 Si 2.0 fuller's earth	3.25	621	3
British starter mix	54 KNO$_3$ 40 Si 6 charcoal	3.30	560	3
Black powder, A5		3.95	457	4
British thermit mix	65 British starter mix 22 Fe$_2$O$_3$ 13 Al (grained)	5.49	545	5
Red lead starter	48.1 Pb$_3$O$_4$ 48.1 Mn 3.8 Si	6.33	625	6
Red lead starter	78.1 Pb$_3$O$_4$ 20.8 Mn 1.1 Si	6 (approx.)		No ignition

IGNITION THEORY

Although tests that reliably measure ease of ignition under particular circumstances have practical value, the development of an analytical model of the ignition mechanism is of utmost importance. A literature search revealed that D.M. Johnson[3] has treated such a model, beginning with the basic equation for heat transfer and the proposed definition of ignition temperature as "that temperature to which a given solid composition must be heated to ignite and continue to combust without further heating by an external source." He derived an equation which helps to determine the effect of pertinent variables on ignition. The following derivation, for which the present author assumes responsibility, is similar in outline and direction to Johnson's, but follows a quite different path. The fact that both treatments arrive at the same equation tends to confirm its validity.

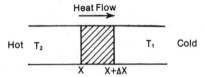

Consider a slab of a substance bounded by a region of high temperature T_2 at x and a region of low temperature T_1 at $x + \Delta x$. The temperature difference produces a flow of heat (H) as shown in the illustration. The change in the heat content of the slab with time t equals the difference between the rates of heat flow into and out of the slab:

$$-KA \left.\frac{\partial T}{\partial x}\right|_x + KA\left.\frac{\partial T}{\partial x}\right|_{x + \Delta x} = \frac{\partial H}{\partial t} \tag{1}$$

where K is the coefficient of thermal conductivity and A is the area of each face through which the heat flows. But:

$$\frac{\partial H}{\partial T} = PA \Delta xC \frac{\partial T}{\partial t} \tag{2}$$

where P is the density, Δx is the slab thickness and C is the specific heat.

Substituting (2) into (1) and expanding the second term in (1) by Taylor's series give:

$$-KA \left.\frac{\partial T}{\partial x}\right|_x + KA\left\{\left.\frac{\partial T}{\partial x}\right|_x + \frac{\partial^2 T}{\partial x^2} \Delta x\right\} = \rho A \Delta xC \frac{\partial T}{\partial t} \tag{3}$$

The first two terms in (3) cancel each other. Dividing both sides of (3) by $A \Delta x$ yields:

$$K \frac{\partial^2 T}{\partial x^2} = C \frac{\partial T}{\partial t}$$

or

$$\frac{\partial T}{\partial t} = \frac{K}{\rho C} \frac{\partial^2 T}{\partial x^2} \tag{4}$$

If we let the diffusivity α equal $K/\rho C$, (4) becomes:

$$\frac{\partial T}{\partial t} = \alpha \frac{\partial^2 T}{\partial x^2} \qquad (5)$$

which is the basic heat equation.

We now solve this equation in order to determine the slab temperature at any given time. To do so, we assume ideal conditions: the entire slab surface ignites simultaneously, there is no radiant heat loss, and the container does not contribute to heat conduction.

Let the slab temperature be a function of a variable y:

$$T = T(y) \qquad (6)$$

where:

$$y = xt^n \qquad (7)$$

We can now calculate the terms in equation (5), first imposing the restriction that every xt product can be expressed as a power of y. Thus:

$$\frac{\partial T}{\partial t} = \left(\frac{\partial T}{\partial y}\right)\left(\frac{\partial y}{\partial t}\right) \qquad (8)$$

By differentiating (7), we obtain:

$$\frac{\partial y}{\partial t} = nxt^{n-1} \qquad (9)$$

so that (8) becomes:

$$\frac{\partial T}{\partial t} = nxt^{n-1} \frac{\partial T}{\partial y} \qquad (10)$$

Similarly:

$$\frac{\partial T}{\partial x} = \frac{\partial T}{\partial y} \frac{\partial y}{\partial x} \qquad (11)$$

and:

$$\frac{\partial^2 T}{\partial x^2} = \left(\frac{\partial^2 T}{\partial y^2}\right)\left(\frac{\partial y}{\partial x}\right)^2 + \left(\frac{\partial T}{\partial y}\right)\left(\frac{\partial^2 y}{\partial x^2}\right) \qquad (12)$$

From (7), we determine that:

$$\frac{\partial y}{\partial x} = t^n \tag{13}$$

so that:

$$\left(\frac{\partial y}{\partial x}\right)^2 = t^{2n} \tag{14}$$

and

$$\frac{\partial^2 y}{\partial x^2} = 0 \tag{15}$$

Substitute (15) and (14) into (12) to obtain:

$$\frac{\partial^2 T}{\partial x^2} = \left(\frac{\partial^2 T}{\partial y^2}\right)\left(t^{2n}\right) + 0 \tag{16}$$

Substituting (16) and (10) into the heat flow equation (5) gives:

$$\frac{\partial T}{\partial y} nxt^{n-1} = \alpha \, t^{2n} \frac{\partial^2 T}{\partial y^2} \tag{17}$$

Dividing both sides of (17) by nxt^{n-1} yields:

$$\frac{\partial T}{\partial y} = \frac{\alpha}{nxt^{-n-1}} \frac{\partial^2 T}{\partial y^2} \tag{18}$$

Applying the restriction that every xt product is a power of y, it follows that xt^{-n-1} must be the first power of y because the exponent of x is 1. Consequently, $xt^{-n-1} = xt^n$, $n = -n-1$, and $n = -1/2$. Equation (18) now becomes:

$$\frac{\partial T}{\partial y} = \frac{\alpha}{(-1/2)xt^{-1/2}} \frac{\partial^2 T}{\partial y^2} \tag{19}$$

Since $y = xt^n = xt^{-1/2}$, (19) becomes:

$$\frac{\partial T}{\partial y} = -\frac{2\alpha}{y} \frac{\partial^2 T}{\partial y^2} \tag{20}$$

or:

$$\frac{\partial^2 T}{\partial y^2} = -\frac{y}{2\,\alpha}\,\frac{\partial T}{\partial y} \tag{21}$$

To aid in the solution of equation (21), we define a parameter P such that:

$$P = \frac{\partial T}{\partial Y}$$

Then:

$$\frac{dP}{dy} = -\frac{y}{2\,\alpha}\,P \quad \text{or} \quad \frac{dP}{P} = -\frac{y}{2\,\alpha}\,dy \tag{22}$$

Integrating (22) gives:

$$\ln P = -\frac{y^2}{4\,\alpha} + C_1 \tag{23}$$

or:

$$P = \frac{dT}{dy} = C_1 e^{-y^2/4\,\alpha} \tag{24}$$

which when integrated gives:

$$T = C_1 \int_m^n e^{-y^2/4\,\alpha}\,dy + C_2 \tag{25}$$

Now let $Z^2 = y^2/4\,\alpha$, so that $Z = y/2\sqrt{\alpha}$. Since $y = xt^n = xt^{-1/2}$, we get:

$$Z = x/2\,\sqrt{\alpha t} \tag{26}$$

Substituting (26) into (25) gives:

$$T = C_1 \int_m^n e^{-Z^2}dZ + C_2 \tag{27}$$

Values of m and n can be obtained by analyzing (26) as follows:

$$
\begin{aligned}
\text{as } t &\to \infty, & Z &\to 0 \\
\text{as } t &\to 0, & Z &\to \infty \\
\text{as } x &\to 0, & Z &\to 0 \\
\text{as } x &\to \infty, & Z &\to \infty
\end{aligned}
$$

Therefore, the lower limit m is zero and n can assume any value between zero and infinity, namely $x/2\sqrt{\alpha t}$. Equation (27) then becomes:

$$
T = C_1 \int_0^{x/2\sqrt{\alpha t}} e^{-Z^2} \, dZ + C_2 \tag{28}
$$

We now evaluate the constants C_1 and C_2. As time t approaches infinity, the temperature T approaches the ignition temperature T_i. Since the upper limit of integration in equation (28) approaches zero as t approaches infinity, we have:

$$
T_i = C_1 \int_0^0 e^{-Z^2} \, dZ + C_2 \tag{29}
$$

so T_i equals C_2, and (28) becomes:

$$
T = C_1 \int_0^{x/2\sqrt{\alpha t}} e^{-Z^2} dZ + T_i \tag{30}
$$

As time t approaches zero, the temperature T approaches the ambient value T_a and Z approaches infinity. Under these boundary conditions, (30) becomes:

$$
T_a - T_i = C_1 \int_0^\infty e^{-Z^2} dZ = C_1 \sqrt{\pi}\,/2 \tag{31}
$$

The value of the definite integral can be found in the Handbook of Chemistry and Physics, 60th edition (CRC Press, Boca Raton, Florida), p. A-95, integral No. 663. Thus, from (31) we have:

$$
C_1 = 2(T_a - T_i)/\sqrt{\pi} \tag{32}
$$

Substituting (32) in (30) gives:

$$
T - T_i = \frac{2(T_a - T_i)}{\sqrt{\pi}} \int_0^{x/2\sqrt{\alpha t}} e^{-Z^2} \, dZ \tag{33}
$$

or:

$$\frac{T - T_i}{T_a - T_i} = \frac{2}{\sqrt{\pi}} \int_0^{x/2\sqrt{\alpha t}} e^{-z^2} \, dZ \tag{34}$$

Differentiating (34) confirms that it is a valid solution to the heat equation (5). Equation (34) also corresponds exactly to the equation derived by Johnson. It interrelates the ignition temperature T_i, the temperature T at an intermediate point x in the slab at time t, the ambient temperature T_a (obviously lower than T and T_i), and the diffusivity $\alpha = K/\rho C$.

Johnson solved the equation for T and differentiated to obtain the temperature gradient at a point x within the length of a column of pyrotechnic material:

$$\frac{\partial T}{\partial x} = \frac{T_a - T_i}{\sqrt{\pi \alpha t}} e^{-x^2/4\alpha t} \tag{35}$$

where t is greater than zero and the point at a distance x into the pyrotechnic composition is not at either end.

We can now substitute (35) into the one-dimensional heat flow equation:

$$q_{in} = - KA \frac{\partial T}{\partial x} \tag{36}$$

where q_{in} is the rate of heat flow into the material. This gives:

$$q_{in} = KA \frac{(T_i - T_a)}{\sqrt{\pi \alpha t}} e^{-x^2/4\alpha t} \tag{37}$$

When an equilibrium condition occurs so that T is constant (the temperature at the point x in the material stops changing), the quantity $x/2\sqrt{\alpha t}$ must also equal some constant:

$$x/2\sqrt{\alpha t} = G \tag{38}$$

Then:

$$x^2 = 4G^2 \alpha t \tag{39}$$

$$2x \frac{\partial x}{\partial t} = 4G^2 \alpha$$

$$\frac{\partial x}{\partial t} = 2G^2 \alpha / x \tag{40}$$

This is tantamount to saying that the rate of burning, $\partial x / \partial t$, is the same as the rate of propagation of a surface of constant temperature T.

Substituting (39) into (37) causes the exponential to reduce to e^{-G^2}. This is simply a constant which we will call F. Equation (37) now becomes:

$$q_{in} = \frac{KAF(T_i - T_a)}{\sqrt{\pi \alpha t}} \tag{42}$$

which we can solve for t, the time to ignite from a constant heat flow q_{in}:

$$t = \frac{K^2 A^2 F^2 (T_i - T_a)^2}{\pi \alpha q_{in}^2} \tag{43}$$

But the diffusivity α equals K/PC. So (43) becomes:

$$t = \frac{K P C A^2 F^2 (T_i - T_a)^2}{\pi q_{in}^2} \tag{44}$$

If we define the ignition energy E for a pyrotechnic mix as

$$E = q_{in} t$$

and substitute for t in (44), we get:

$$E = \frac{K P C A^2 F^2 (T_i - T_a)^2}{\pi q_{in}} \tag{45}$$

The equation for ignition time tells us a number of physical facts that generally conform with expectations based on both experience and intuition. The time is longer if the thermal conductivity is high (heat dissipates rapidly), if the density is high (more mass to heat), if the specific heat is large (more heat required per unit mass to raise the temperature), if the cross-sectional area is large (contributes to both mass and heat loss), and if the T_i is high (greater temperature rise is required). Ignition time is shorter if q_{in} is high because more heat is available to raise the temperature.

This analysis shows clearly that Henkin-McGill ignition times are unlikely to be accurate because of the important effects of density and area on the measurements. The Johnson equation is applicable to pyrotechnic problems to some extent, e.g., to calculate the difference between the energies required to ignite a mix at high and low temperatures. If the T_i of a certain mix is 300 °C, then the ratio of ignition times at 30° and −50 °C is:

$$\frac{^t30\,°C}{t-50\,°C} = \frac{(300 - 30)^2}{(300 + 50)^2} = \frac{72,900}{122,500} = 0.6$$

which also indicates that the energy required to ignite the mix at the warmer temperature is only 60% of that required for ignition at the colder temperature.

The ignition equation also illustrates the dire effects of underignition. If only part of the mix ignites, it generates heat more slowly. According to the equation, cutting the heating rate in half quadruples the ignition time. Thus, loosely packed spots in a nonuniformly compressed mix, heat conduction losses through the container, or a diminished burning area can lower the heat supply rate below the level needed for continued steady burning, and cause duds or erratic burning times.

Rearrangement of the ignition equation to:

$$B(T_i - T_a)^2 = (\text{Energy Factor})^3$$

also permits a comparison of the ignition sensitivity of pyrotechnic mixes. Table II shows calculated Energy Factors for several mixes (black powder is arbitrarily assigned the value of 1.00) together with ignition temperatures. Note that the lower Energy Factor for the Pb_3O_4-Mn-Si mix implies that it is more sensitive than black powder in spite of its higher ignition temperature. This agrees with the finding of McLain and Frahm that the red-lead mix is easier than black powder to ignite with hot sparks.

Table II. Pyrotechnic energy factors		
	T_i °C	Energy Factor
Black powder	321	1.00
Pb_3O_4-Mn-Si	458	0.36
B-PbO_2-Viton	300	0.61
B-$BaCrO_4$	655	23.6

Overignition

In 1957, a liquid O_2-powdered Al demonstration experiment, described by the catalog as safe, sure, and easy, was performed in the Indiana University Chemistry Auditorium before visiting high school students. The supposedly benign mixture detonated and hurled fragments from two iron dishes and a stone tabletop throughout the auditorium. The toll was a lost eye, a broken arm, a broken ear drum, and severe face and body lacerations.

Under more controlled conditions, Austin et al[4] tested the effect of three different levels of initiation in a series of experiments. The results were:

Initiator Strength	No. of Trials	Type of Detonation
High	8	4 high order, 2 low order, 2 flares
Medium	5	1 high order, 1 low order, 3 flares
Low (hot wire)	13	3 high order (starting as 2-sec flares), 1 low order, 9 flares

These events, both deliberate and inadvertent, demonstrate the hazards of overignition.

Reaction temperature

In the early days of solid state chemistry, reaction temperature was a much-used concept. Its definition is related to the reaction conditions. At the beginning of an exothermic reaction, the heat of reaction is dissipated to the surroundings. When the point is reached at which the rate of heat loss falls behind the rate of heat generation, the temperature of the reactant mass rises appreciably. The temperature rise increases the reaction rate which, in turn, accelerates heat evolution. The reaction proceeds uncontrolled until slowed by the accumulation of solid products, the moderation of the temperature rise by equilibrium between heat gains and losses, or the depletion of reactants. By definition, the reaction temperature is that at which the runaway increase in reaction rate begins. It is indicated by a marked change in slope of a graph of temperature versus time for a mix heated slowly under controlled conditions.

Pressure and critical mass

The runaway reaction rate is pressure dependent. In fact, the basic difference between explosive detonation and burning is that detonation reflects a faster rate of propagation caused by reaction of the explosive at high pressure as well as over a large inner area of the reaction zone.

When granular explosives such as tetryl, TNT, and PETN are ignited, the amount of burning reactant must exceed a *critical mass* to enable the transition to detonation. Initiator explosives such as lead azide, tetrazine, and lead styphnate have a small critical mass even at atmospheric pressure because their extremely fast burning rates rapidly transform the reacting solids into gaseous products which self-pressurize the reaction zone. Several pyrotechnic formulations can also progress from burning to detonation at atmospheric pressure. A notable example is the 4:1:1 $KClO_4$-Al-Sb_2S_3 flash-and-sound mix; 200 mg, lit from fuse spit in an open cup, produces a high-order detonation.

Figure 4 demonstrates the importance of pressure in propellant ignition. All four propellants tested required less ignition energy at higher pressures.

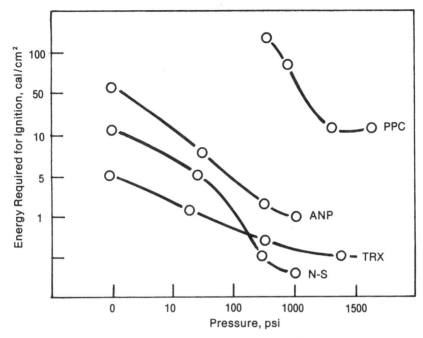

Figure 4. *Effect of pressure on energy required for ignition. TRX is a composite polysulfide with* NH_4ClO_4. *N-S is an extruded double base. PPC contains butadiene, methyl vinyl pyridine, and* NH_4NO_3. *ANP consists of polyurethane and* NH_4ClO_4.

Powling, of the Explosives Research and Development Establishment at Waltham Abbey, Essex, England, was the first to determine the burning mechanism that leads to high-pressure ignition in nitrate ester propellants (probably also applicable to other pressurized mediums). He established that the reaction proceeds by a free-radical mechanism and that departures from continuity were caused by the appearance of NO, a well-known free-radical "grabber." The sequence is seen in the hypothetical pressure-vs-time curve in Figure 5.

At first ignition, the pressure rises at a moderate rate which steepens if autocatalytic burning occurs. In the case of the nitrate ester propellant, NO accumulates, slowing the reaction, and the pressure levels off. When the NO is used up, the propellant grain reignites. Since the temperature and pressure are now higher than they were initially, the reaction rate is higher and the pressure rises faster than before. The sequence repeats itself and the pressure rises stepwise to detonation in a very short time. If a high pressure igniter is used, the reaction proceeds from the initial pressure P_I directly to explosion.

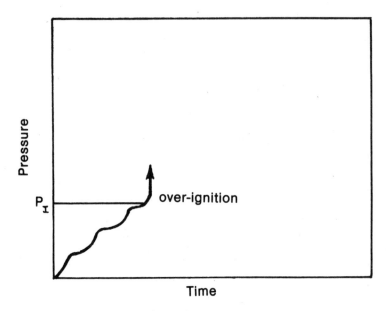

Figure 5. *Hypothetical pressure-time ignition curve.*

Thermal conductivity and *K* factor

Other conditions influence the runaway reaction rate. One is thermally conductive container walls. For example, NH_4NO_3-C fuel blocks pressed into cans for the AN-M7 floating smoke pot occasionally exploded. Observation of burning fuel blocks showed that ignition was planar, but burning proceeded faster down the side of the metal container than through the center. This enlarged the burning surface, increased the pressure in the confined volume, and progressed to explosion. A chipboard liner added to the bottom and sides caused the pressure-time curve to change from A to B in Figure 6 and overcame the explosion problem.

Both thermal conductivity and *K* factor affected a series of tests of an MK-24 55:45:8 Mg-NaNO₃-laminac flare mix pressed at 1500 psi into a 3-inch pipe nipple assembly shown in Figure 7. The *K* factor, defined as the ratio of burning surface area to nozzle throat area, was 26 (relatively large). Although the flare mix was not believed to be an explosion hazard, it is a very high heat producer (see Chapter VII), and the experiment was designed to evaluate the possibility that burning could grow to detonation.

Three test units were ignited by remote control and all underwent high-order detonation (12,000-16,000 f/sec) in 3 sec or less. Evidently, burning along the walls increased the surface area; the already large *K* factor was effectively increased and indicated a relatively small vent for the rising pressure; and the confinement promoted an increase in pressure and temperature, which accelerated the reaction to the point of explosion.

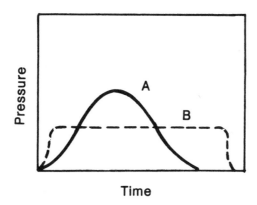

Figure 6. *Pressure-time characteristics of* NH_4NO_3*-C fuel blocks before (A) and after (B) insertion of an insulating liner in the metal housing.*

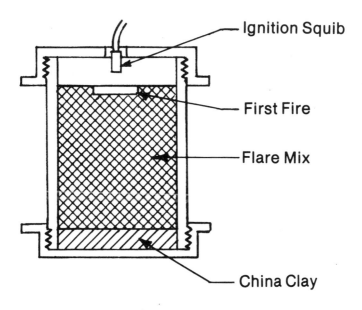

Figure 7. *Assembly for testing explosive potential of flare mix.*

Hot spots

Premature detonation can also originate at hot spots. A reactant mass undergoing exothermic decomposition is hotter inside than on its surface. If the reaction rate increases with temperature according to the relationship:

$$k = Ae^{-E_a/RT}$$

then too slow a heat loss will prevent establishment of steady-state conditions because the reacting mass will self-heat until the rate reaches an explosive level. The condition for explosion by self-heating for a semi-infinite slab of explosive is, according to Ubbelohde[5]:

$$(E/RT_0^2)(d^2w/K)Ae^{-E_a/RT_0} \geq 0.88$$

where d is half the thickness of the slab, K is the thermal conductivity, and $w = Q/\rho$, the heat of reaction per unit volume. This self-heating phenomenon requires special care to avoid escalation to explosion in high caloric solid mixes, especially those containing $KClO_3$. For some reactions, Q (therefore w) is so high and E_a so low that very small masses can explode.

In studies of detonation sensitivity, the addition of grit particles or micro-balloons to solid explosive mixes and the presence of bubbles in liquid explosives greatly increased the sensitivity. These localized the temperature rise and created spots hot enough to detonate the explosive in the immediate vicinity, which then detonated the larger mass[6]. Hot spots are like the thermal analog of nicks in steel springs that concentrate mechanical stresses and cause premature fatigue failures.

Practical suggestions to aid ignition

- Use stepped or serrated rams to consolidate the surface to be ignited.
- Use slag-forming starters.
- Vent to prevent gas blocking.
- Use incandescent particles in the primer.
- Do not use starter mixes that have a large flameproof residue.
- Use an enriched mix as a relay link to the main mix.
- Tailor the ignition mix to the system.

Of a good beginning cometh a good end.
John Heywood

Chapter XIII

REFERENCES

1. Henkin, H. and McGill, R., *Ind. and Eng. Chem.* **44**, 1391 (1952).

2. McLain, J.H. and Frahm, A.L., *A New Method of Comparing Ignition Sensitivity of Pyrotechnic Mixtures,* T.D.M.R. 882, Edgewood Arsenal, Md., 1944.

3. Johnson, D.M., *Ignition Theory: Application to the Design of New Ignition Systems,* RDTR No. 56, U.S. Naval Ammunition Depot, Crane, Ind., 1965.

4. Austin, C.M., Rohrer, C.S., and Seifert, K.L., *J. Chem. Ed.* **36**, 54 (1959).

5. Ubbelohde, A.R., *Melting and Crystal Structure,* Clarendon Press, Oxford, 1955; Chapter 11.

6. Bowden, F.P., in *4th Symposium (International) on Combustion,* Williams and Wilkins, Baltimore, 1953; pp. 161-171.

Chapter XIV

METALS, ALLOYS, AND INTERMETALLIC COMPOUNDS

A virtue to be serviceable, must like gold, be alloyed with some common but more durable metal.

Samuel Butler

Many metals and metallic substances are used in pyrotechnic compositions. Table 1 gives a partial list. As a class, these materials have distinct physical properties such as luster, high electric and thermal conductivity, and mechanical ductility and malleability. It is their chemical electropositivity that is of primary interest to chemists and pyrotechnicians, but their physical properties are also important.

For example, large surface area (small particle size) is often necessary for pyrotechnics and explosives. Al can be readily powdered by atomization or ball milling, but the ductility and malleability of Mg present greater difficulty. However, the compound Al_3Mg_4 is quite frangible and easily ground into a powder of the desired particle size. The compound also has unique chemical properties. Obviously, the interatomic forces in the compound are different from those in the constituent metals.

How does this affect the chemical properties? Does the heat of combustion of 1 mol of Al_3Mg_4 equal that of 3 gram atoms of Al and 4 of Mg, or is it less or more? The literature[1] is not consistent on this question, investigators variously reporting the heat of formation to be -780, -4110, or -7000 cal/g atom. Phase diagrams indicate that the compound forms with a definite atomic ratio and has less heat of reaction than an equivalent mixture of the constituent metals.

Table I. Metals and alloys used in pyrotechnics

Metal or Alloy	Property or Application
Ag, Bi, Cr, Fe, Mo, Ni	Delays
B, Mn, Si, Ti, W	Starters and delays
Cu	Heat conductor, blue and green stars
Mg	Flares
Sb	Delays and white stars
Zn	Fireworks and smoke
Zr	Heat mixes, white sparks, starters, primers
Al-Pd	Pyrofuze
Be-Cu	Nonsparking tools
$CaSi_2$	Starters and self-heating food cans
Ce-La-Nd (misch metal)	Tracer bullets and lighter flints
Ce-Pb	Sparking alloy
Hg-Al	Stress cracking
Ni-Al	Pyronol torch
Ni-Zr(with $KClO_4$)	Delays
Pb-Zr	Lighter flints

Another variable aspect of metal behavior is the effect of dopants. In Chapter IV, the dopants discussed tended to contaminate or distort the crystal structure and thus weaken the lattice to achieve desired properties of reactivity or semiconductivity. This is not always the case. For example, doping Fe with C produces a steel that is stronger than the original Fe. The C atom has the right size to fit into structural interstices and the Fe-C bond is stronger than the Fe-Fe bond, which makes it possible to produce such hard, dense materials as tool steel.

INTERMETALLIC COMPOUNDS

Intermetallic compounds have not been explored as thoroughly as some other areas of chemistry, possibly because of the absence of a great unifying

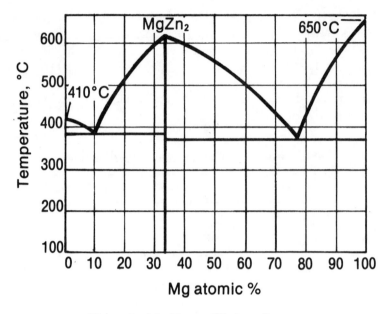

Figure 1. Mg-Zn *equilibrium diagram.*

theory of valence applicable to metals comparable to the theory that explains the bonds in so many other compounds. Readers are advised to study the pertinent literature[1,2,3].

Equilibrium diagrams are indispensable for determining the formation of compounds, usually indicated by a peak in the curve like that in Figure 1 where the compound $MgZn_2$ forms at approximately 33 atomic percent of Mg. Once it is known that a compound does indeed form and its stoichiometry has been determined, then an attempt can be made to classify the bond. Three general classes of bonding are recognized.

Semi-ionic bonding

One group of metal-metalloid compounds is characterized by semi-ionic bonding, so called because it most resembles the more familiar ionic bonding.

Examples include:

Ca_2Si Mg_2Pb
Mg_3Bi Mg_2Si
Mg_3Sb_2 Zn_3Sb_2
Ca_3As_2 Mg_2Sn
Ba_2Pb Cu_3Al

Laves "Size Factor" compounds

A large group of binary intermetallic compounds with the general formula AB_2 have a particularly stable spatial arrangement. If the ratio of the two atomic diameters is approximately 1.2:1, the unit cell is cubic and contains 24 atoms. The smaller atoms lie at the corners of tetrahedra joined apex to apex, leaving dodecahedral interspaces into each of which a larger atom fits. There are three main types of Laves compounds:

MgCu₂ type	MgZn₂ type	MgBi₂ type
$CaAl_2$	$BaMg_2$	$HfCr_2$
KBi_2	$CaCd_2$	$HfMn_2$
$TiBe_2$	$FeBe_2$	$ReBe_2$
$ZrFe_2$	$ZrCr_2$	
ZrW_2	$TiFe_2$	

Chemical properties of Laves compounds are sensitive to changes in the size of adulterant metals and the number of electrons per atom.

Hume-Rothery compounds

Hume-Rothery[3], also known as electron, compounds are intermetallics which have similar structures with apparently unrelated stoichiometry but the same ratio of valence electrons to number of atoms. For example, the beta phases of the Cu-Zn, Cu-Al, and Cu-Sn systems all have cubic close-packed crystal structures and the molecular formulas are $CuZn$, Cu_3Al, and Cu_5Sn, respectively. If Cu is univalent, Zn bivalent, Al trivalent, and Sn quadrivalent, the Hume-Rothery condition can be demonstrated:

Compound	Valence Electrons	Number of Atoms	Ratio
$CuZn$	$1 + 2 = 3$	2	3/2
Cu_3Al	$3 + 3 = 6$	4	3/2
Cu_5Sn	$5 + 4 = 9$	6	3/2

Others in the 3/2 class are Cu_3Bi, $AgZn$, $AgMg$, and Ag_3Al.

For gamma alloys, the situation becomes:

Compound	Valence Electrons	Number of Atoms	Ratio
Cu_5Zn_8	$5 + 16 = 21$	13	21/13
Cu_9Al_4	$9 + 12 = 21$	13	21/13
$Cu_{31}Sn_8$	$31 + 32 = 63$	39	21/13

Fe_5Zn_{21} is also considered in the 21/13 class, but Fe is assigned 0 valence electrons to maintain the class ratio. The same is true for Co, Ni, Rh, Pd, Pt, and, presumably, Os, Ir, and Ru.

Assuming these zero-valence metals, what would the structure of Ni-Al and Pd-Al combinations be? From the above, the most stable forms should be:

Compound	Valence Electrons	Number of Atoms	Ratio
NiAl	0 + 3 = 3	2	3/2
PdAl	0 + 3 = 3	2	3/2

characterized by beta phases and A2 (body-centered cubic) structure.

Can these metals form other compounds? Ni_6Al_7 might be a Hume-Rothery compound since the ratio of electrons to atoms is $(0 + 21)/13 = 21/13$ as for the gamma phase compounds listed above. However, this is unlikely because the atomic ratio is too close to 1:1. On the other hand, the atomic diameters are 1.283, 1.154, and 1.248 for Pd, Ni, and Al, respectively, so that Laves compounds $PdAl_2$ and $AlNi_2$ may be possible.

Special intermetallic applications

A 79.81% Pd, 20.19% Al system, corresponding to the compound formula PdAl, is marketed under the name *Pyrofuze* and widely applied in pyrotechnics and explosives. Among its advantages as a delay and ignition material are reproducibility, no need for mixing, pressing, or waterproofing, long-term storage stability, and small volume. Its heat of alloying is 327 cal/g (3263 cal/cm³) and its ignition temperature is 670 °C (Al melting point = 660 °C). Pyrofuze is available in wire, sheet, or granular form. The wire is made by swaging Pd cladding over an Al core.

Other exothermic alloying reactions are also of pyrotechnic interest, e.g., the 68.5% Ni, 31.5% Al (NiAl compound) powder used in a modified thermite mix to increase heat and speed. Heat of alloying is 329 cal/g (2290 cal/cm³). Kubaschewski and Catterall[1] give the heat of NiAl formation as 17,000 cal/mol at 293 °K and state that it is "obviously due to the new covalent bonds formed between dissimilar atoms." Suitably cased and directed, this reaction can cut through 4 inches of stainless steel in 0.25 seconds. The Ni-Al combination reacts only in a powder mixture, not as wire or sheet. An 87.5% Pt, 12.5% Al mixture reacts very much like the Pd-Al system above, but the important characteristic, its heat of alloying, is only 216 cal/cm³.

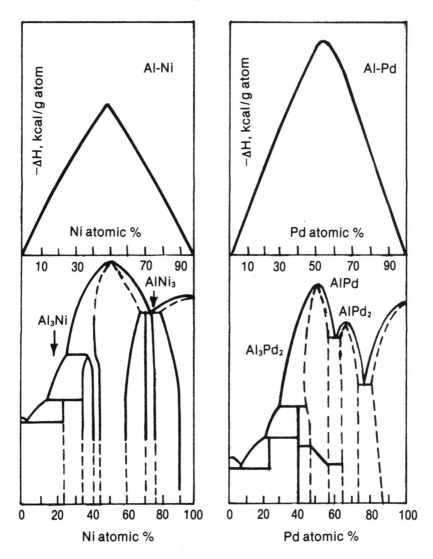

Figure 2. Al-Ni *and* Al-Pd *equilibrium diagrams*[4].

Ferro and Capelli[4] have investigated the Al-Ni and Al-Pd systems and determined equilibrium diagrams and heats of alloying. Compounds formed (see Figure 2) include Al_3Ni, $AlNi$, $AlNi_3$, Al_3Pd_2, $AlPd$, and $AlPd_2$. A recent German patent substitutes an Al-Pd *Pyrofuze* alloy for the conventional copper, brass, or aluminum in metal cones for shaped charges and claims significantly increased penetration.

Since reactions involving metals, alloys, and intermetallic compounds depend so much on the altered forms and imperfections of solids, they permit almost endless variation and will undoubtedly be exploited in the future in possibly surprising ways.

Looking over solid state science and taking account not only of its own history but that of science as a whole, I am inclined to believe that it is still a very rich field for future work and will continue to be exciting as long as man has any direct interest in condensed matter. Fortunately, the unquestioned practical importance of the field seems to guarantee that it will receive a great deal of attention at a fundamental level. This would seem to guarantee the presence of the critical minimum of stimulating minds.

Frederick Seitz, 1963

Chapter XIV

REFERENCES

1. Kubaschewski, D. and Catterall, J.A., *Thermochemical Data of Alloys*, Pergamon Press, London and New York, 1956; pp. 31 and 32 and citations.
2. Pauling, L., *Nature of the Chemical Bond and the Structure of Molecules and Crystals: An Introduction to Modern Structural Chemistry*, 3rd ed., Cornell University Press, Ithaca, N.Y., 1960.
3. Hume-Rothery, W., *Electrons, Atoms, Metals and Alloys*, Dover, New York, 1963.
4. Ferro, R. and Capelli R., *Rendiconti dell' Accademia dei Lincei* 34, 659-664 (1963).

Chapter XV

METHODS AND TECHNIQUES

It is now almost my sole rule of life to clear myself of cants and formulas.

T. Carlyle

So much of the performance of pyrotechnics depends upon how the ingredients are processed, including mixing, granulating, binding, drying, loading, and pressing, yet the literature contains few detailed discussions of methods. Formulae are always necessary but never sufficient to accomplish the desired effects. Good recipes don't always make the best cooks.

Processing is not only important to performance, but also influences ease of manufacture, loading, and safety. Some valuable mixes could not be used if appropriate mixing, granulating, and pelleting techniques had not been developed. Remote mixing techniques must also be available to protect personnel from the hazards of fire, explosion, and toxic dust.

PREPARATION OF RAW MATERIALS

The first operation in the making of pyrotechnics is generally considered to be mixing. Actually, mixing cannot begin until the basic ingredients have been properly prepared. This involves several procedures.

Grinding

Grinding, usually by micropulverizer (essential equipment for almost all pyrotechnic operations), not only decreases particle size and increases active surface area, but also ensures that each batch is prepared the same way. This promotes consistency, uniformity, and reproducible performance. To accomplish this, the micropulverizer must be set for a proper feed rate and screen size. The standard operating procedure for all inorganic oxidizers is to dry, micropulverize no more than two days before use, and then dry again.

Ball milling

Ball mills also serve to reduce particle size. These are still used in some processes, notably the milling of black-powder premix and the preparation of metal powders, but mill charging and discharging are time consuming and sometimes dangerous. Results are difficult to control and vary considerably with material properties such as frangibility and hardness.

Neither the ball mill nor the micropulverizer should be used to mix a flammable pyrotechnic. Nor should they be used interchangeably for oxidizers and reductants, since small residues of the one can react with the other. Terrible accidents have been followed by, "I thought it was clean!"

Coating

Before the advent of corrosion-resistant metals such as Ti and Zr, it was common practice to coat metal powders such as Mg, Fe, and Zn as protection against deterioration. The fireworks industry stirred the powders with wooden paddles in large, shallow, steam-heated cast-iron bowls filled with paraffin, linseed oil, rosin, or various combinations of these coating materials. Stearic acid has been added to the list of coatings, and solutions of newer synthetic resins such as polyvinyl chloride are now applied by dipping or spraying.

Heat treatment

Experience has shown that heat treatment enhances the uniformity of processed material. The effect of calcining ZnO on the properties of HC smoke mix was discussed in Chapter VI. $PbCrO_4$ and $BaCrO_4$ provide other examples. As received from paint pigment producers, these chromates presumably contain water soluble or volatile components that affect performance even if present in only small amounts. After washing, filtering with suction, and heating to 400 °C for at least 4 hours, chromate performance improves and batch-to-batch variations diminish.

MIXING

If not actually the first operation, mixing is generally regarded as the most

important one in the pyrotechnics industry. The method of combining ingredients varies with the mix as required to obtain optimal results.

Hand screening

Hand screening is probably as old as fireworks and is still a mainstay of
the industry. Figure 1 shows a typical double mixing trough, and Figure 2
shows a hand mixing screen. The dry ingredients are weighed and placed on
the screen which is set over one of the troughs. Using both hands, the mixer
spreads the material back and forth over the screen with long, sweeping motions, only occasionally letting the edge of the hand come in contact with the
screen. From time to time, the mixer taps the screen with fingertips to open
the pores.

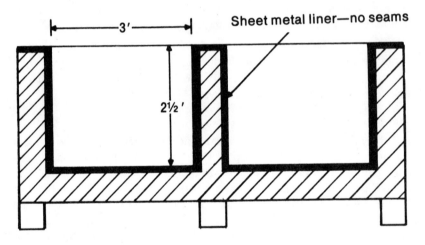

Figure 1. *Double-tub trough for screen mixing pyrotechnic powders.*

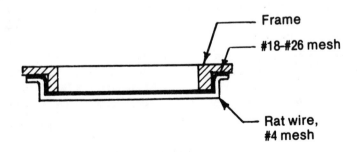

Figure 2. *Hand mixing screen.*

When all the material has passed through the screen, the screen is moved to the second trough, the screened material is scooped up and placed on the screen, and the process is repeated. Four or five passes through a 22 mesh screen gives an excellent mix. Adequacy of mixing is determined by a smear test in which the mix is spread under fingertip pressure. If no streaks of individual ingredients appear, the mix is considered satisfactory.

Screen mixing by hand seems crude, laborious, and ineffective, but is none of these. Its primary drawback is danger to the mixer in case of a spark. It should not be used for highly sensitive mixes nor for those containing toxic ingredients such as lead salts.

Brush screening

To screen mix without exposing personnel to the hazards of fire and toxic dust, banks of three remotely operated brush screeners like that in Figure 3, similar to flour sifters, have been assembled, one screener above another. The rotating brushes are pulley driven from a drive shaft connected to a motor located outside the building. Ingredients are weighed and placed in the topmost unit. The motor is actuated by remote switch and the screenings are collected in a box positioned under the bottom screener. For successive screenings, the contents of the box are emptied into the top screener and the process is repeated. Two or three passes yield excellent results. For safety, all screens must be wired together and to a common ground.

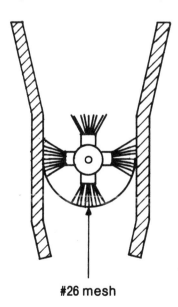

#26 mesh

Figure 3. *Remotely operated brush screener.*

Mechanical mixing - dry

Type C smoke premix, composed of ZnO and hexachlorethane, has been successfully mixed with a comminuting machine, a swing rotating hammer mill operating at a fairly high speed. The comminuting machine is particularly effective with heavy, easily agglomerated powders, but is much too rough for anything but relatively inert materials.

Several methods have been used to add powdered Al to the premix, including double-cone blenders, dough mixers, and rumblers (50-gallon milk cans with interior baffles), with varying degrees of success. Rumbling is most efficient, followed, in descending order, by dough mixers and double-cone blenders. However, as demonstrated by past accidents, any bladed mixer can cause a fire, especially if tramp metal and/or grit are scraped against the side of the mixer. The form of dough mixer called the ribbon blender should never be used for a pyrotechnic mix.

Mechanical mixing - wet

The $NaNO_3$-Mg-laminac illuminating flare mix is mixed with a Simpson Intensive Muller or a Lancaster Mix Muller, both wet processes. The mullers, which operate on the same principle as the wheel mill used in black-powder manufacture (see Chapter IX, Figure 1), consist of a central rotating shaft and two wheels with plowshares inside each wheel. The wheels revolve around an axis perpendicular to the drive shaft within the cylindrical body of the mixer. Because the illuminating flare mix is quite tacky, mullers are essential to achieve the necessary thorough mixing.

Another piece of equipment used for high-viscosity mixes is the sigmoid blade mixer, based on a principle similar to that of a dough mixer. As its name implies, this device involves the rotation of an S-shaped blade within a closed horizontal cylinder.

The Hobart is an effective and versatile mechanical mixer in which a motor-driven stirrer both spins and precesses. With a suitable choice of motor speed and stirrer configuration, it is usable for mixes with consistencies ranging from a thin gruel to a heavy dough.

Other mechanical mixers have also been used, which combine various elements of the above machines and sometimes include vibrating screens.

Coprecipitation

The outstanding contribution of C.H. Miller and R.J. Benge has already been mentioned[1]. Their coprecipitation process consisted of the addition of a $K_2Cr_2O_7$ solution to a large beaker of hot (about 90 °C) $Ba(NO_3)_2$ solution in which fine particles of B were suspended. During efficient stirring, $BaCrO_4$ precipitated around and on the B particles. This coprecipitated B-$BaCrO_4$

mix had the unique quality of burning at the same rate at widely different ambient pressures (see Table III, Chapter IV). The explanation of this property is not fully understood, but it is hypothesized that the close bonding between the reductant and oxidant precludes atmospheric oxygen from entering into the reaction. Thus, pressure has little effect and the mix burns more slowly but at a constant rate.

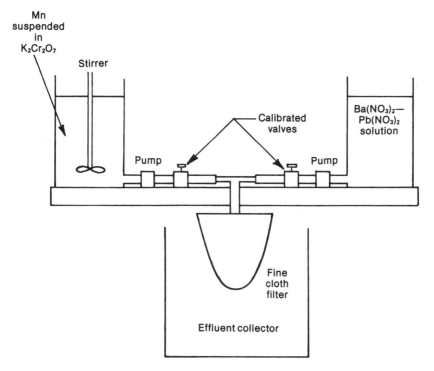

Figure 4. *Washington College coprecipitation assembly[2].*

After learning of the Miller and Benge results, the author's group at Washington College, Chestertown, Maryland set up a similar but significantly different coprecipitation assembly as shown in Figure 4[2]. We chose for our first study the D-16 Manganese Delay Mixtures invented by R.H. Comyn[3], which have outstanding low-temperature ignition and propagation properties and a wide range of burning rates, depending on composition:

Mn, %	44	39	37	33
$BaCrO_4$, %	3	14	20	31
$PbCrO_4$, %	53	47	43	36
Burning rate, in/sec	0.25	0.17	0.12	0.075

The goal of our first run was a 37:20:43 Mn-BaCrO$_4$-PbCrO$_4$ mix with a burning time of 0.12 in/sec. Chemical analysis showed the resulting composition to be within 1% of the goal for all three ingredients. Burning rate in tubes loaded with the dried and pressed mix was 0.15 in/sec, slightly faster than the mechanical mix of the same proportions, but was uniform within 2% from tube to tube.

One essential difference between the two coprecipitation arrangements, judged important according to written comments by Miller and Benge, is the higher temperature at which they carried out their reaction. Another is the extreme variation in concentration gradients inherent in their process. The first addition of dichromate solution to the barium solution, no matter how well stirred, can be likened to adding a drop of ink to Lake Erie, and the last addition is like a drop of water in a sea of ink. Since crystal size and shape depend on concentration gradients as well as on temperature, the BaCrO$_4$ first precipitated can differ widely from the last. The more consistent conditions of the Washington College coprecipitation apparatus can be an important improvement of the original concept.

Coprecipitation also offers a good method for doping oxidizers and, with the incorporation of altervalent ions in the barium and/or lead solutions, for modifying the burning rates of delay mixes.

Coacervation

One of the dictionary definitions of coacervation (to form an aggregate of colloidal droplets) approaches but does not encompass its use here. The label seems to have originated in a 1929 DeJong and Kruyt paper as a replacement for the word "unmixing" in a description of colloidal systems. Although possibly a misnomer, coacervation is a useful process which should be more widely applied in the future. It is a form of coprecipitation based on a different solubility principle from that of the Miller and Benge and Washington College processes.

In pyrotechnics, coacervation depends on the ability of ethyl alcohol to preempt the solvent capacity of water. Soluble ionic compounds form stable solutions in water because of hydration. For example, a Na$^+$ ion is surrounded by ion-dipole-bonded water molecules. More than one layer of water molecules can become attached to the ion, but the attractive force diminishes rapidly with layer number. Anions such as NO$_3^-$ and SO$_4^{2-}$ attract the positive ends of the dipolar water molecules, and oxygen in the anion will even form a weak hydrogen bond.

It is the enveloping water shells that prevent reassociation and thus stabilize the solution. The innermost layer of water molecules clinging to the cation becomes part of the hydrated crystal, for example, in Na$_3$PO$_4$·12H$_2$O, Na$_2$SO$_4$·7H$_2$O, and Na$_2$SO$_4$·10H$_2$O. The strength of the cation-water or ion-dipole bond is proportional to the charge on the ion and inversely proportional to the square of the ionic radius. Transition metals are generally more strongly hydrated than are pretransition metal ions because electron-pair bonds add to the ion-dipole attraction.

Ethyl alcohol molecules bond more strongly to the water molecules than do the cations. Consequently, addition of the alcohol to a water solution of salt strips the ions of their protective coat and causes reassociation or precipitation. Two examples will illustrate the application of coacervation to pyrotechnics.

In the preparation of a Mg-NaNO₃ illuminating flare mix, a saturated solution of $NaNO_3$ containing suspended Mg powder is pumped into one arm of a Y-tube to join a stream of absolute ethyl alcohol introduced through the other arm[4]. A $NaNO_3$ precipitate in the form of a wet mush intimately mixed with the Mg flows out of the trunk of the Y through a fine cloth filter. (Some thought has been given to the use of downstream cooling coils to increase the yield of solid $NaNO_3$, but this has not yet proved to be necessary.) The wet mixture is dried, laminac added, and the combination is blended in a muller. The advantages of this process are a shorter mixing time, elimination of the necessity for micropulverizing the $NaNO_3$, and the possibility of conversion to a continuous operation with the addition of an alcohol recovery unit and a movable filter-dryer.

A similar coacervation procedure is used to make Australian delays. In this case, a solution of $K_2Cr_2O_7$ containing suspended B and Si is combined in a tube with a stream of alcohol. A wet-mush mixture of $K_2Cr_2O_7$, B, and Si is precipitated, collected, dried, loaded into lead tubing, swaged, and cut to desired lengths. This dichromate mix has the unique property of a constant burning rate at widely different temperatures at two predetermined pressures.

METHODS FOR HIGHLY HAZARDOUS MIXES

Dry mixing in individual containers

Barrel rumbling. To prepare a Sb_2S_3-Al-$KClO_4$ flash-and-sound mix, the premixed Sb_2S_3 and Al are gang spooned into individual tubes with sealed bottoms. Trays of these partially loaded tubes are then taken to another building where freshly ground and dried $KClO_4$ is spooned in to complete the load and the top of the tube is sealed with a cap or a silicate cement. The filled, but unmixed, tubes are then dumped into a large barrel half full of dried sawdust, the barrel is closed, and the building is vacated. At a remote location, no less than 50 yards away, a switch is then thrown to start the motor that rotates the barrel at 30 to 40 rpm for 15 minutes. This method of mixing a highly dangerous mix in individual containers was used for ten years with good results and no accidents. A similar method is now used in the fireworks industry.

Rubber cup mixer. Stab primers may contain the most sensitive of all pyrotechnic mixes. One such mix, containing $KClO_3$, carborundum, Sb_2S_3, and dextrinated $Pb(N_3)_2$, must be mixed and loaded as a dry powder. An effective mixer was constructed of a 500-ml conductive rubber cup inside which four $\frac{1}{4}$ x $\frac{1}{4}$ x 5-inch wooden baffles were cemented with 90° spacings. The cup was loaded with the powder, clamped with its axis tilted about 20° off the vertical, and rotated at 40 to 50 rpm. Ten minutes was sufficient. The drive motor and switch were remotely placed for safety.

Three other highly sensitive primer mixes were successfully mixed in the rubber cup:

	NOL 130 %	NOL 60 %	PA 101 %
Basic lead styphnate	40	60	53
$Pb(N_3)_2$	20		
Tetracene	5	5	5
$Ba(NO_3)_2$	20	25	22
Sb_2S_3	15	10	10
Al powder			10

Corey jigglers. Mixing in individual containers, effective and safe for flash-and-sound mixes, also solved the problem of mixing and loading photoflash mixes of $Ba(NO_3)_2$, $KClO_3$, and Al which had a history of disastrous accidents with loss of lives. An engineer-machinist named Corey at Pace Manufacturing Company in Memphis, Tennessee devised machines that subjected the packaged photoflash mix to vibrations of frequencies and modes predetermined to accomplish the desired mixing. Use of the remotely operated Corey *Jigglers,* as they were known, enabled Pace to produce photoflash munitions for over eight years with a perfect safety record.

Wet mixing

High speed blending. A novel Zr-PbO_2-tetracene primer mix for a delay detonator was not only hazardous to handle, but also required exceptional homogeneity to ensure the desired performance. Variations of as little as 0.25% in tetracene content had a large effect on delay time. Since all three ingredients are insoluble and unaffected by water, it was decided to mix them in a water suspension, first with a high-speed laboratory propeller-stirrer, then with a modified Waring blender. Both produced excellent dispersions.

An important requirement of such wet mixing is quick filtration before the suspension can stratify. Buchner funnels with maximum-flow filter paper and water-pump suction worked well in this case. After the filter cake was dried on paper, it was broken up in a small, remotely operated brush screener. Since this mix is exceedingly sensitive to ignition by static sparks, extra grounding was a necessary precaution.

Polymer precipitation. During the mid-1960s, pyrotechnicians at the Naval Weapons Center, China Lake, California, developed a composition with a $(C_3H_2F_4)_x$ fluorocarbon polymer binder. The unique method of mixing the composition and incorporating the binder has come to be known in the trade as the *wet mix* or *polymer-precipitation* process. At its simplest, this process involves dissolving the polymer in a solvent, adding the dry ingredients and stirring vigorously, then adding a nonsolvent to the system to cause precipitation, or "kick-out," of the mix. It is a form of acervation.

In the late 1960s, pyrotechnicians at the Naval Weapons Support Center, Crane, Indiana used polymer precipitation to mix B-PbO_2, red-phosphorus-containing compositions, and others quite dangerous to mix by other means. The author is indebted to Mr. Duane M. Johnson of the Naval Weapons Support Center and Mr. Victor G. Willis of the Crane Army Ammunition Activity for the following details of the procedure.

There are three phases: pre-gel, gel, and post-gel. In the pre-gel phase, the system first consists of the polymer dissolved in solvent. Dry ingredients are added, and the solution is stirred with a high-shear blade that insures good flow in the container and keeps insolubles from settling out. After dispersion is satisfactory, a non-solvent (relative to the polymer and dry ingredients) is added slowly. When the non-solvent:solvent ratio reaches a critical value characteristic of the particular system, a gel forms, manifested by a curdled appearance at the surface of the solution. Two liquid phases are now present: the non-solvent and solvent, and the solvent and polymer.

While more non-solvent is added to the gel phase, solvent is continually extracted from the solvent-polymer liquid, increasing the polymer concentration. After addition of sufficient non-solvent, all of the solvent is extracted, leaving the polymer and pyrotechnic mix behind as a precipitate in the post-gel phase. If the polymer, solvent, and non-solvent have been properly selected, the dry ingredients will have remained homogeneously dispersed and will now be uniformly coated with precipitated polymer. The solution can be decanted off and the composition flash-dried and readied for use.

The beauty of this process is that concern for safety is focused on the choice of the solvent and non-solvent rather than on the dry ingredients. The pyrotechnician receives an end product that is homogeneous and requires no screening. This is a special benefit with compositions that are hazardous to screen because of friction sensitivity.

However, some precautions are necessary before using the polymer-precipitation process:

Dry ingredients must be insoluble in the chosen solvent and non-solvent.

The mixing container must be covered to minimize solvent evaporation and associated cooling.

After liquid is decanted from the post-gel phase, the mix must be dried at a temperature above the local dew point.

The following are details for preparing red-phosphorus compositions with this technique, using three very different polymers as examples, a fluorocarbon, an epoxy, and a urethane.

POLYMER-PRECIPITATION MIXING OF
RED-PHOSPHORUS COMPOSITIONS

Polymer: Viton A (Dupont fluorocarbon)
1. Weigh out desired amount of binder into powder tank.
2. Add the desired weight of red phosphorus.
3. Stir with rubber spatula until phosphorus is wet.
4. Insert mixer blade and stir until mix appears homogeneous.
5. Lift blade from mix and add each of the other ingredients while stirring with the rubber spatula.
6. Insert mixer blade and stir until mix appears homogeneous.
7. Using a 1.55 hexane:acetone ratio, calculate the amount of hexane needed to cause coacervation.
8. Add half this amount rapidly through a buret at maximum flow rate.
9. Add the other half at a slower rate.

10. Stir for about 5 minutes.
11. Dump hexane quickly into the mix.
12. Add at least 3 volumes of hexane to acetone and wash for at least 10 minutes.
13. Decant, add 3 more volumes of hexane, and wash for 10 minutes.
14. Decant and place mix in pan to air dry. (Drying temperature should be high enough to prevent moisture condensation on mix.)

Polymer: Estane 5702 (B.F. Goodrich polyurethane)

Use same procedure as with Viton A but change hexane:acetone ratio to 0.66 for step 7.

Polymer: Epoxy

1. Place in the tank at least 4 volumes of hexane for each volume of solids.
2. Into the hexane, pour the desired weight of fuel, oxidizer, and phosphorus, stirring slowly with the mixer blade.
3. Weigh out the desired amount of epoxy into a glass beaker.
4. Add 2 volumes of acetone for each volume of epoxy to dissolve the epoxy.
5. Stir the mix at high blade speed and add the acetone-epoxy solution slowly and uniformly.
6. Stir for 10 minutes at high speed.
7. Slowly decrease the speed until the blade can be removed from the mix without spattering.
8. Decant the liquid and place the mix in a pan to air dry. Press before the epoxy hardens.

GRANULATION

Dry powders must often be treated to make pyrotechnic compositions flow and pack freely for safe, efficient, and reproducible loading. One means is granulation, a traditional technique in fireworks and pharmaceuticals, which usually involves addition of a binder.

For example, a PbO-Si delay mix is mixed by hand or a Hobart mixer with a 4% solution of celluloid in acetone. More acetone may be added to increase fluidity. Mixing continues until the solids are completely wetted and the mix is uniformly dough-like. The wet mix is placed on a drying tray and acetone is allowed to evaporate until the mix becomes crumbly but will still form a ball if squeezed tightly in a fist. If too wet, the mix will clog the pores of the granulating screen during the next stage. If too dry, it will be full of dust. With a little experience, a worker can easily judge when a mix is ready for granulation.

The granulation procedure consists of rubbing the mix lightly with the hands on a 20-mesh screen backed by heavy wire over a mixing tub (see Figures 1 and 2). Since the material is slightly wet, the bottom of the tub should be covered with Kraft paper to prevent sticking. When the batch is finished, the mix can be lifted out on the paper and given a final drying to the desired free-flowing granular state. After two or three batches, a novice develops the "feel" that guides the granulation procedure.

Adhesive binders are not absolutely necessary. A skilled technician can granulate almost any mix by wetting with water alone, partially drying, and then rubbing the mix through a screen when it reaches the right consistency. For example, this was advantageous with the PbO_2-Zr delay mix which could not have a gas-forming binder because it was used in a sealed assembly. The mix was wetted with water and worked in a Hobart to a heavy dough. Without binder, less force must be used against the granulating screen, and the granules will be less uniform and less stable. However, they will still be able to flow under gravity at a fairly constant rate.

Granulation after addition of binder can also be performed remotely in brush screens (Figure 3).

PELLETING

For convenient and accurate loading, pyrotechnic mixes can be shaped into pellets of uniform size and weight. A charge is then measured out in terms of a given number of pellets. Any granulated material, with or without binder, can be pelleted with an automatic pelleting press. Granules consolidated by a binder will form hard, strong pellets of virtually constant weight. Pellets made of binderless granules will not be as strong or as uniform in weight, but will still be adequate for use on a loading line, affording much greater efficiency than scoop-loading of unpelleted material. A rotary pellet press can produce 300 pellets per minute. Addition of 0.3% graphite to the granulated mix minimizes abrasive wear of the pelleting rams.

Fireworks stars are made by a wet-pelleting process called bumping. The mix, containing a binder such as dextrin dissolved in water or red gum dissolved in alcohol, is forcibly spread over a perforated brass plate resting on a smooth, solid brass base plate. Some material enters the cylindrical holes. The operator then positions a brass ramming plate with cylindrical studs over the perforated plate so that the studs mate with the holes. Holding the ramming plate by lug-type handles, he rocks it with a seesawing action, "bumping" the mix into compressed discs at the bottom of the holes. More mix is added and the procedure is repeated until the discs form pellets of the desired size. The upper two plates are then raised together and pressure on the ramming plate ejects the pellets onto a paper-lined drying tray.

SWAGING

Granulation is not only necessary for pelleting, but also facilitates other filling operations. In one application, for example, a lead tube is filled with the granules, the tube ends are closed, and the tube is rolled under pressure (swaged) to reduce its diameter and increase its length while the granules compact uniformly in the core. The elongated tubing can then be cut to desired lengths with minimal risk of powder spills from the open ends of the segments.

WOUND FUSE

Delay and fireworks fuses are made by wrapping thread around a descending powder core. In most fuse-making machines, the thread passes through the tip of a funnel containing granulated black powder. If the powder were not granulated to flow uniformly, the powder core would vary in diameter or density, causing large variations in delay time, and could develop gaps that would produce duds.

FILLING METHODS

Single load

Volumetric measurement of loading charges is an industry-wide practice for everything from primers and detonators to candles and rockets. The most primitive volumetric method is spooning. Loading spoons are usually made of soft aluminum so that they can be bent to suit the operator. The operator dips the spoon forward into the loose mix in a rubber cup, shown in Figure 5, raises the filled spoon, and scrapes off the excess powder against the taut rubber band on the backstroke. Operators on a detonator loading line can spoon 12,000 100-mg charges per shift with 2% accuracy.

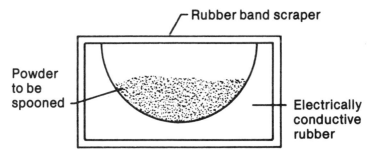

Figure 5. *Conductive rubber cup for spoon filling.*

Another old method, based on the tumbler principle, was first used in the Ideal powder loader. A cylinder with a variable slot is rotated to position the slot under a powder column for filling, and is then rotated 180° (slot down) for discharge.

Gang filling

The above filling methods are suitable only for single charges. The fireworks industry also loads and presses candles and rockets by the gross with devices known as shuttleboards (called measuring boards by the British), as shown in Figure 6, which may be made of phenolic-impregnated canvas

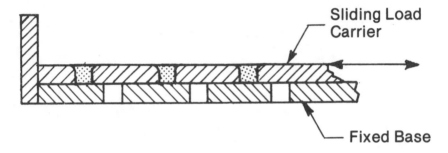

Figure 6. *Shuttle board for loading stars.*

board. In candle loading, for example, an operator measures and drops the clay charge, black powder, stars, and candle mix by filling the cylindrical holes in the upper, sliding board with each charge in turn, and then sliding the board until the upper holes line up with the holes in the base board.

> . . . *the mighty have no theory of technique.*
>
> Leonard Bacon

(This may be true of Art, but should not be said of pyrotechnics.)

Chapter XV

REFERENCES

1. Miller, C.H. and Benge, R.J., *Development of Initiating and Igniferous Materials for Use in Extreme Conditions,* WAA/189/10, E.R.D.E., Waltham Abbey, Essex, England, and British Patent 1,333,551 (1978).
2. Pagliughi, D.J., *Coprecipitated Delays and Methods for Doping,* Senior Thesis, Washington College, Chestertown, Md., 1970.
3. Comyn, R.H., U.S. Patent 2,832,704 (1958).
4. Howlett, S., "A Continuous Process for Mg-NaNO₃ Flare Mix," private communication, 1968.

Chapter XVI

SAFETY

As soon as there is life,
there is danger.
    R. W. Emerson

In them and in ourselves
our safety lies.
    W. Shakespeare

Pyrotechnics has a unique safety problem, if not in character certainly in degree. Accidents can and do happen in all industries, but only in pyrotechnics (extended here to include explosives) is a relatively minor accident so likely to trigger such a large consequence. For this reason, every pyrotechnics worker must be alert and informed as to the inherent hazards and the recommended practices that maximize safety; and building use must be controlled for the safest distribution and restriction of personnel and hazardous material handling. Personnel who work in pyrotechnics plants must live with this peril every hour of every day.

The preparation and use of pyrotechnic materials require an assessment of two factors: the probability of accidental ignition or premature reaction, and the likely extent of the ensuing damage to personnel and property. The first part of the analysis entails measurements of the sensitivity of materials to such ignition sources as impact, friction, sparks (including static electricity), shock, flame, heat, a striking bullet, light, and radio waves. The second has to do with energy output and its consequences.

The measured sensitivities must be relevant to the circumstances and the treatment and handling the materials must undergo. For example, bullet-impact sensitivity is certainly not significant for the mixing and granulating of first-fire compositions in the plant, nor is card-gap sensitivity important for smoke and incendiary mixes. On the other hand, sensitivity to electric spark, friction, impact, heat, and such disturbances is extremely important throughout manufacture, storage, and transportation. Knowing the sensitivities pertinent to the process would warn that it is foolhardy to use an oscillating granulator on a chlorate mix, to mix boron compositions with ungrounded equipment, or to compress impact-sensitive material with high-speed rams. Armed with appropriate foreknowledge, the pyrotechnician must select or design a process that minimizes the probability of premature initiation.

The second step in hazard evaluation is estimation of the type and extent of damaging output from a pyrotechnic accident. The different significances of sensitivity and output have been confused in the past. For example, on learning that the 80:20 PbO-Si delay mix being prepared was 50% more sensitive than TNT to friction and impact, a contractor barricaded the mixing building and limited the amount of mix to two-thirds the TNT quantity. This was absurd because ignition of that particular mix would not produce blast damage. The protection was inappropriately related to sensitivity rather than output.

J.E. Settles[1] emphasized important points about output in a ten-year summary of accidents in the industry presented at a conference on *Prevention of and Protection against Accidental Explosion of Munitions, Fuels and Other Hazardous Mixtures*. In 81 accidents involving propellants and explosives, 103 persons were injured, 78 fatally. Among the accidents:

23 were fires only, causing damage principally by radiant heat.

44 combined fire and explosion.

14 produced supersonic shock waves classifiable as detonations, killing 34 persons and injuring 1. Blast overpressure accounted for only 1 death, and that indirectly, by hurling the victim head-first into a masonry wall. The other 33 deaths were due to flying fragments or heat.

The summary demonstrates that even detonations damage mainly by fragments and heat, and this is even more true of pyrotechnics accidents if explosives are excluded from consideration. Settles criticizes the "fire hazard only" classification (determined by card-gap test) for "reactions of such violence and destructive energy as medium rate detonations, low velocity detonations, high rate explosions, medium rate explosions and even reactions that do not explode but kill people by burning them to death."

The pyrotechnics industry should adopt and be governed by the philosophy that accidents are inevitable. Various accident probabilities can be estimated by statistical analysis of sensitivity and process data, but however small a probability is, cursory consideration shows that an accident will occur sooner or later due to human error or some unforeseen event. For example, assume that the probability of an accident is 1 in 10,000,000 operations. If each of 40 workers performs 5 operations on a pyrotechnics item and produces 3000 items per day, the total is 600,000 operations per day and 3,000,000 per 5-day week. On the average, that production line can expect to have a little over 1 accident per month.

Emphasis must then be placed on safety design to prevent injuries to personnel and, as far as is economically feasible, to minimize damage to facilities when an accident happens. Specific output data are needed to do this. What kind of protection is best for personnel? Should this protection guard against shock wave, overpressure, and sympathetic detonation between buildings, as might be expected with detonable substances, or against fragments, radiant heat, smoke inhalation, toxic fumes, or suffocation?

QUANTITY-DISTANCE TABLES FOR EXPLOSIVES

Tables and graphs have been devised that express the relationship between the quantity of explosive material and the maximum distance at which it is likely to do serious damage if it explodes. How much protection is afforded by regulations based on these tables and do they have a sound basis? Is there such a thing as a safe distance? To rephrase the question, Is there a zero-risk distance for explosives, propellants, and pyrotechnics? Since a precise answer is unlikely, we must undoubtedly expect a graph of quantity-distance requirements to consist of an envelope rather than a single line.

What else should we expect the graph to be? Certainly, zero amount of explosive requires zero distance for safety, so the curve must start at the origin. Is the curve linear? The answer is no, based on the intuitive expectation that the wave of destruction expands in a roughly spherical fashion. The intensity would then decrease approximately in proportion to the expanding spherical surface over which the destructive energy is distributed, that is, as the square of the distance. Therefore, at twice a given distance we would expect the destructive intensity to be only one-fourth as great. By this crude estimate, it would take four times the amount of explosive to double the safe distance. Consequently, we would expect the quantity-distance curve to have the general shape shown in Figure 1.

Marshall[2] has reviewed the historical development of this subject in considerable detail. He states that the movement started in 1908 in Germany with the prescription of a quantity-distance relationship for buildings in nitroglycerine plants. Great Britain followed in 1909, and in 1910 a group of American manufacturers constructed a table based on a study of the damage

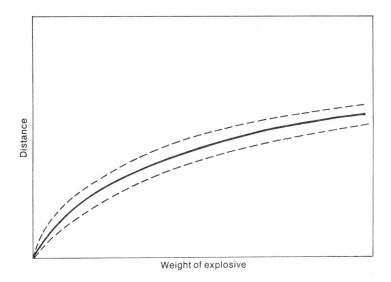

Figure 1. *General shape of quantity-distance curves for explosives.*

caused by known accidental explosions. The graphs in Figure 2 compare the early British and American tables with the latest (1976) U.S. Department of Defense (DOD) - North American Treaty Organization (NATO) table.

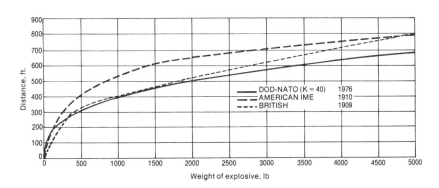

Figure 2. *Quantity-distance curves for explosives, based on tables from various sources*[2,3,4].

The British not only gave building specifications, but for the first time divided possible targets into two categories:

    1. *Railway, Aerodrome, Canal (in active use) or other navigable water, Dock, Pier, or Jetty; Market Place, Public Recreation and*

Sports ground or other open place where the public are accustomed to assemble; Public highway, Private road which is a principal means of access to a Church, Chapel, College, School, Hospital or Factory; River wall, Sea wall, Reservoir.

2. Dwelling House, Retail Shop; Government and Public Buildings, Church Chapel, College, School, Hospital, Theatre, Cinema or other building where the public are accustomed to assemble; Factory; Building or works used for storage in bulk of petroleum spirit, gas or other inflammable substances; Building or works used for the storage and manufacture of explosives or of articles which contain explosive.

Figure 3 shows quantity-distance curves for the highest hazard category (ZZ) and for the two target categories. The most stringent requirements are applied to the second target category. The British attempt to take into account the nature of the target in determining acceptable distances is valuable, but naturally complicates the quantity-distance relationship.

In 1919, French authorities applied the formula $d = KW^{1/2}$, in which d is the distance in meters, K is a constant that depends on explosive output, type of storage, and target category, and W is the weight of explosive in kg. France was the first country to differentiate among the various explosives by assigning different values of K:

7.5 chlorate explosives
5.0 nitroglycerine
3.5 black powder
2.5 ammonium- and sodium-nitrate explosives
1.5 cartridges of black-powder pellets

The 1976 DOD-NATO safety standards were calculated with a similar formula, $d = KW^{1/3}$, in which d is now in ft and W is in lb. Assigned K factors for Class 1, Division 1 materials and inhabited building targets were:

Net explosive weight, lb or Location	K
0-100,000	40
100,000-250,000	40, increasing to 50
250,000-15,000,000	50
Public traffic route	24
Intraline distance - barricaded	9
- unbarricaded	18

Figure 4 shows curves for various values of K.

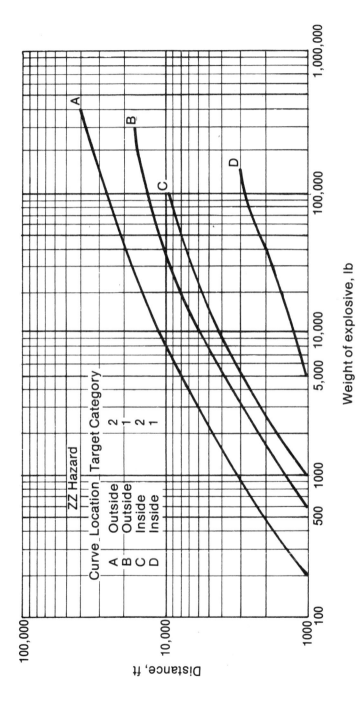

Figure 3. *British quantity-distance relationships for the highest hazard category and various targets* [3].

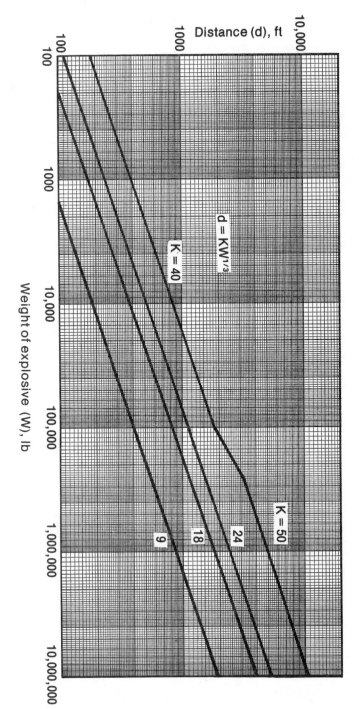

Figure 4. *DOD-NATO 1976 quantity-distance graphs for various explosive output factors*[4].

R. Assheton has also compiled all available information on accidental explosions throughout the world, and Robinson[5] selected 100 of these for further study with the results shown in Figure 5. Two of the findings are especially significant. The average distances for serious damage from barricaded and unbarricaded sources are not appreciably different; and the Ordnance Safety Manual (OSM) intraplant distances are always less than the average serious-damage distance. Robinson observes that the intraplant distances are an "expectation to kill."

Robinson also reasoned that barricades are a dubious requirement at best because the data associate them with increased missile throw. This is true for high explosives and even more so for propellants and other normally less explosive pyrotechnical materials which involve containment. Containment of large quantities of burning substance promotes increased pressure, faster reaction rates, and higher temperature and supplies the fragments for missiles. Therefore, complete containment is neither practical nor desirable except for very small quantities. Robinson's suggestion to barricade the targets rather than the donors should be followed up. It makes sense particularly for intraplant operations where a building occupied full time may be completely destroyed with great loss of life. Figure 5 shows that the $9\,W^{1/3}$ required distance is inadequate for safety because it is less than the average distance at which damage is serious whether the donor is barricaded or not. We might paraphrase Robinson's suggestion as "Let's protect the people not the stores."

Bringing order to this complex safety problem may be difficult, but both theoretical and empirical approaches lead to the same conclusions. Some steps that may help to make our plants and environs safer to work in and live near are:

- Design explosives buildings with a blowout wall and roof section, constructed as flimsily as possible, that will prevent excessive pressure buildup and will not fragment into missiles capable of traveling more than 50 yards.
- Use two-part donor building construction including a reinforced concrete wall at least one-foot thick extending at least six feet above the blowout roof line.
- Aim the blowout wall at vacant land, a suitably protected building, or an uninhabited building containing inert stores.
- Recognize the differences among explosives and weight the required distances accordingly.
- Retain the sound DOD-NATO standards based on explosive weight and a public-traffic-route location, but increase the intraline distances.
- Protect target buildings.

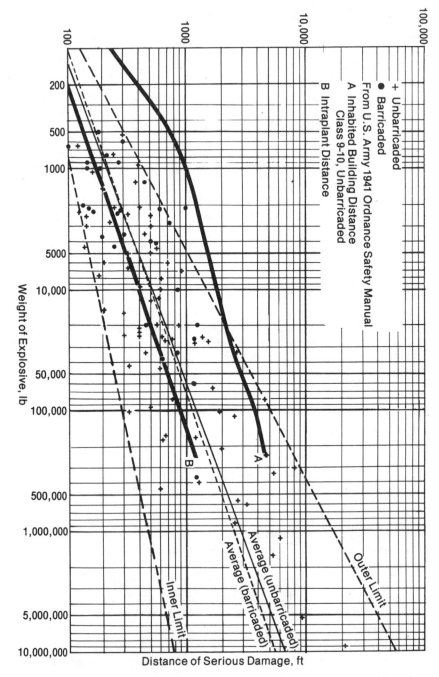

Figure 5. *Empirical quantity-distance data based on 100 accidental explosions*[5].

PYROTECHNICS SAFETY

It is useful to distinguish between explosives and pyrotechnics for safety purposes. In general, pyrotechnics are more sensitive than explosives to spark and flame and less sensitive to shock and impact. The degree of confinement of pyrotechnics by packaging, building, or barricade plays a primary role in the potential for damage. (However, the widespread belief is mistaken that no pyrotechnic mix can undergo a high-order explosion unless confined by packaging.) On the other hand, shock can induce a high-order detonation of a detonable explosive even in the form of loose powder.

Also, pyrotechnics are complex mixtures the explosive properties of which vary widely with such factors as particle size of the ingredients, the oxidant-reductant ratio, porosity (pressed or unpressed condition), as well as the degree of confinement. Explosives are generally chemical compounds and/or relatively simple mixtures with added aluminum and wax.

Thus, explosives and pyrotechnics have very different output and initiation characteristics and require different protective methods not adequately covered by present quantity-distance tables intended for explosives. Also, the tables were developed largely as an attempt to make explosives, propellants, and their packages safer and more reliable during transportation, storage, and use, and have little to do with safety during manufacture. The author makes the following proposal to help remedy the situation for pyrotechnics.

Proposed classification of pyrotechnics

This proposal applies two criteria: output and sensitivity. Output hazard is rated by a number from 6 (most hazardous) to 1 (least hazardous). Sensitivity is designated by a letter from A (most sensitive) to D (least sensitive). Thus, 6A presents the greatest and 1D the least hazard. Since output and sensitivity of pyrotechnic mixes depend so much on composition, that is, the ratio of oxidizer to fuel, mixes are identified by both the ingredients and their common name or use when assigned a hazard rating.

Output ratings were more difficult to assign than sensitivity ratings. Sensitivity is relatively easy to measure in the laboratory. Output is not so easy to measure and is influenced by such variables as critical mass, confinement, method of initiation, porosity, and ambient temperature. Fortunately for this task, although unfortunately for those suffering losses, there have been accidents and impromptu tests that supply information. One example is experience by the fireworks industry with Class C Common Fireworks. During the past ten years, six trailer loads carrying 25,000 to 30,000 lb of such fireworks as packaged Roman Candles, small rockets, and fountains have caught fire and burned without explosion. Many of the output classification numbers derive from data obtained from such accidents.

This proposed classification also adds military pyrotechnic mixes to the fireworks previously included in a safety analysis that resulted in the National Fire Protection Association publication NFPA 44A, *Manufacture, Transportation and Storage of Fireworks*. The author was a member of the committee which prepared that comprehensive study so that a similarity of wording between the present proposal and NFPA 44A is readily understandable. The following classification tables expand the ideas developed for fireworks. Tables 1, 2, and 3, referred to in the classification tables, are included at the end of this chapter before the list of references.

PYROTECHNICS HAZARD CLASSIFICATION TABLES
CLASS 6

Characteristics
Detonates from open burning.
Small critical mass.
Very sensitive to spark and friction.
Capable of sympathetic detonation.

Required precautions
Storage and transportation: Apply Table 1, *American Table of Distances for Storage of Explosives* (Class 7 DOD and / or Class A DOT).
Production: Mix and load remotely. Protect personnel by reinforced concrete at least one foot thick. Building should have breakaway (blowout) construction of the opposite wall and roof. Mix whenever possible in final package by such means as rumbling or vibration. Exercise extreme care to avoid spark from static electricity.

MIX	NAME and/or USE	CLASSIFICATION
$KClO_3$, Al or Mg, Sb_2S_3	Salute mix	6A
$KClO_3$, Al, S	Salute mix	6A
$KClO_3$, Al, As_2S_3	Salute mix	6A
$KClO_3$, C, S	Chlorate explosive	6A
$KClO_3$, S, sand	Torpedo mix	6A
$KClO_4$, Zr	"Instantaneous" squib, relay powder	6A
$KClO_3$, C, S	Squib	6B
$KClO_4$, Al or Mg	Photoflash	6B
$KClO_4$, Al or Mg, $Ba(NO_3)_2$	Photoflash	6B
$KClO_4$, Al or Mg, S	Flash and Sound, firecracker mix	6B
$KClO_4$, Al or Mg, Sb_2S_3	Flash and Sound, firecracker mix	6B
$KClO_4$, Al or Mg, As_2S_3	Flash and Sound, firecracker mix	6B
PbO_2, Zr or ZrH_4	"Instantaneous" squib	6B
PbO_2, Ti	"Instantaneous" squib	6B
PbO_2, B	"Instantaneous" squib	6B
Pb_3O_4, Zr	"Instantaneous" squib	6B

MIX	NAME and/or USE	CLASSIFICATION
Pb_3O_4, Ti or B	"Instantaneous" squib	6B
$PbCrO_4$, B or Ti	"Instantaneous" squib	6B
Picrate + oxidizer	Whistle mix	6B
Gallate + oxidizer	Whistle mix	6B
Salicylate + oxidizer	Whistle mix	6B

CLASS 5

Characteristics

Relatively unconfined burning, e.g., in open-end mixers or a small building, can produce low-order but destructive explosions.

Very sensitive to spark.

Required precautions

Storage and transportation: Same as for Class 6.

Production: Same as for Class 6 except for batches limited to 5 lb. Amounts of 30 g or less may be used on a loading line.

MIX	NAME and/or USE	CLASSIFICATION
KNO_3, C, S	Black powder	5A
KNO_3, B	Igniter	5A
PbO_2, Si	Millisecond delay	5A
$KClO_4$, Mg	Tracer mix	5B
$Ba(NO_3)_2$, Mg	Tracer mix	5B
$BaCrO_4$, Zr	Heat mix	5B
Fe_2O_3, Zr	Starter Mix	5B
$(C_2F_4)_n$, Mg	IR flares	5B

CLASS 4

Characteristic

Bulk powder subject to deflagration progressing to low-order explosion.

Required precautions

Storage and transportation: Use minimum separation distances in Tables 2 and 3.

Production: Personnel must be shielded during pressing operation. Mixing building should have breakaway construction.

MIX	NAME and/or USE	CLASSIFICATION
$KClO_3$, $NaHCO_3$, S, dye	Military colored smoke	4A*
$KClO_3$, lactose, dye	Military colored smoke	4A*
$BaCrO_4$, Mg	Igniter	4A

MIX	NAME and/or USE	CLASSIFICATION
$PbCrO_4$, Mg, Si	Flash igniter	4A
$KClO_3$, flour, dye	Fireworks colored smoke	4B *
$KClO_4$, Mg, $Ba(NO_3)_2$	Military stars	4B
$KClO_4$, Mg, $Sr(NO_3)_2$	Military stars	4B
$BaCrO_4$, B	Igniter and delay	4B
$NaNO_3$, Mg, binder	Illuminating flare mix	4B
$KClO_4$, Mo	Millisecond delay	4C

*In bulk and unpressed in containers. When pressed and in containers, downgrade to Class 2.

CLASS 3

Characteristic

Fireball large and quick.

Required precautions

Storage and transportation: Use minimum separation distances in Tables 2 and 3.

MIX	NAME and/or USE	CLASSIFICATION
$KClO_4$, salts of Sr, Ba, Na, powdered Al, Mg, or Zn, gums	Fireworks stars	3A
Fe_2O_3, Zr, Ti	Flash igniter	3B
Fe_2O_3, Ti	Starter	3B
$KMnO_4$, Mg	Smoke puff	3B

CLASS 2

Characteristic

Fire hazard to personnel.

Required precautions

Storage and transportation: Use minimum separation distances in Tables 2 and 3.

MIX	NAME and/or USE	CLASSIFICATION
KNO_3, C, S (unmilled)	Candle or rocket mix	2A
PbO_2, Si, CuO	Starter	2A
Pb_3O_4, Fe_2O_3, Si, Ti	Starter	2A
$K_2Cr_2O_7$, B, Si	Delay	2A
$KClO_4$, Al, $Sr(NO_3)_2$, dextrine	Colored sparklers	2A
KNO_3, Al, Fe_3O_4, C, Si	Smoke starter	2B

MIX	NAME and/or USE	CLASSIFICATION
$KMnO_4$, Sb	Delay	2B
$KMnO_4$, Mn	Delay	2B
$NaNO_3$, C, sugar	Starter	2B
$K_2Cr_2O_7$, Ti	Delay	2C
Fe_2O_3, Al, Ni	Pyronol torch	2D

CLASS 1

Characteristic

Slight fire hazard to building and surroundings.

Required precautions

Storage and transportation: Use minimum separation distances in Tables 2 and 3.

MIX	NAME and/or USE	CLASSIFICATION
$KClO_4$, Zr/Ni alloy, $BaCrO_4$	Grenade delay	1A
$KClO_4$, $Sr(NO_3)_2$, S, sawdust	Fusee mix	1A
Pb_3O_4, Si, kaolin	Delay	1A
$KClO_4$, W, $BaCrO_4$	Long delay	1B
$KClO_4$, Cr, $BaCrO_4$	Delay	1B
$KMnO_4$, W, $BaCrO_4$	Long delay	1B
PbO, Si	Delay	1B
$CaSi_2$, Fe_3O_4	Food can heater	1B
Bi_2O_3, B, $K_2Cr_2O_7$	Delay	1B
$BaCrO_4$, $PbCrO_4$, Mn	D16 delay	1C
Bi_2O_3, B	Delay	1C
Fe_3O_4, Al	Thermite	1D
$Ba(NO_3)_2$, Fe, Al, dextrine	Gold sparkler	1D
ZnO, Al, C_2Cl_6	HC smoke (Type C)	1D

FORBIDDEN MIXES

$KClO_3$ and P, $KClO_4$ and P, unless kept wet as in the toy cap process.
$KClO_3$ and S, unless $NaHCO_3$ is added to one or the other; $KClO_3$ and B.

FORBIDDEN OPERATIONS

Do not use oscillating granulators on mixes with A, B, or C sensitivity.

Do not hand screen any Class 1 or Class 2 mix or any mix with A, B, or C sensitivity regardless of class.

Use only electrically interconnected containers when transferring from one to another any Class 1 or Class 2 mix or any mix with A, B, or C sensitivity regardless of class.

Never use water to mix or granulate $KClO_3$-S mix or any mix containing powdered Zn, Al, or Mg. Photoflash and flash-and-sound mixes containing Mg, Al, or alloy and oxidizing agents such as $Ba(NO_3)_2$ and $KClO_4$ have detonated when small amounts of water were admitted to the enclosed mix. Water may be used with mixes containing Ti and Zr and an oxidizer, but only in large quantities at least 20 times the volume of the dry ingredients.

TOXICITY

The above recommendations pertain to fire and explosion hazards. Handlers of pyrotechnic materials should also be aware that all mixes containing lead salts and airborne dusts of Si and other substances are hazardous.

Conclusion

The proposed standards are not the ultimate in pyrotechnics hazard classification. For one thing, they are based on experience and do not apply to mixes not yet developed. Small-scale output tests will have to be devised to classify the relative hazards of future mixes to personnel and facilities. It is hoped that the new ideas expressed and the observations gleaned from over thirty years of involvement with pyrotechnics will promote objectivity and stimulate further effort in this vital area.

Safety is no accident.
Anonymous slogan

Table 1. American Table of Distances for Storage of Explosives
(as revised and approved by The Institute of Makers of Explosives, November 5, 1971. Distances in ft.)

Weight of Explosives, lb		Inhabited Buildings		Public Highways Class A to D		Passenger Railways-Public Highways with Traffic Volume of more than 3,000 Vehicles/Day		Separation of Magazines	
Over	Not Over	Barri-caded	Unbarri-caded	Barri-caded	Unbarri-caded	Barri-caded	Unbarri-caded	Barri-caded	Unbarri-caded
2	5	70	140	30	60	51	102	6	12
5	10	90	160	35	70	64	128	8	15
10	20	110	220	45	50	81	182	10	20
20	30	125	250	50	100	93	186	11	22
30	40	140	230	55	110	168	206	17	24
40	50	150	300	60	120	110	220	14	28
50	75	170	340	70	140	127	254	15	30
75	100	190	380	75	150	139	278	16	32
100	125	200	400	80	160	150	300	18	36
125	150	215	430	85	170	159	318	19	38
150	200	235	470	95	190	175	350	21	42
200	250	255	510	105	210	188	378	23	46
250	300	270	540	110	220	201	402	24	48
300	400	295	590	120	240	221	442	27	54
400	500	320	640	130	260	238	476	29	58
500	600	340	680	135	270	253	506	31	62
600	700	355	710	145	280	266	532	32	64
700	800	375	750	150	300	278	566	33	66
800	900	390	760	155	310	289	578	35	70
900	1,000	400	800	160	320	300	600	36	72
1,000	1,200	425	850	165	330	318	636	39	78
1,200	1,400	450	900	170	340	336	672	41	82
1,400	1,600	470	940	175	350	351	702	43	86
1,600	1,800	480	980	180	360	366	732	44	88
1,800	2,000	505	1,010	185	370	378	756	45	90
2,000	2,500	545	1,090	190	380	408	816	49	98
2,500	3,000	580	1,160	195	390	432	884	52	104
3,000	4,000	635	1,270	210	420	474	948	58	116
4,000	5,000	685	1,370	225	450	513	1,026	61	122
5,000	6,000	730	1,480	235	470	546	1,092	65	130
6,000	7,000	770	1,540	245	490	573	1,145	68	135
7,000	8,000	800	1,600	250	500	600	1,200	72	144
8,000	9,000	835	1,670	255	510	624	1,248	75	150
9,000	10,000	865	1,730	260	520	645	1,290	78	156
10,000	12,000	875	1,750	270	540	687	1,374	82	164

Table 1. *(Continued)*

Weight of Explosives, lb		Inhabited Buildings		Public Highways Class A to D		Passenger Railways-Public Highways with Traffic Volume of more than 3,000 Vehicles/Day		Separation of Magazines	
Over	Not Over	Barri-caded	Unbarri-caded	Barri-caded	Unbarri-caded	Barri-caded	Unbarri-caded	Barri-caded	Unbarri-caded
12,000	14,000	885	1,770	275	550	723	1,445	87	174
14,000	16,000	900	1,800	280	560	756	1,512	90	180
16,000	18,000	940	1,880	285	570	786	1,572	94	188
18,000	20,000	975	1,950	290	580	813	1,626	98	196
20,000	25,000	1,055	2,000	315	630	876	1,752	105	210

Table 2. Minimum separation of pyrotechnic processing buildings, magazines and storage buildings from inhabited buildings, passenger railways, and public highways

(Adapted from *Guide to the Explosives Act, 1875,* as amended, 4th ed., Her Majesty's Stationery Office, London, Appendix K, pp. 223 and 224).

Pyrotechnics net weight, lb	Distance from passenger railways and public highways, ft		Distance from inhabited buildings, ft	
	Class 1 & 2	Class 3 & 4	Class 1 & 2	Class 3 & 4
100	25	200	50	200
200	30	200	60	200
400	35	200	70	200
600	40	200	80	208
800	45	200	90	252
1,000	50	200	100	292
2,000	58	230	115	459
3,000	62	296	124	592
4,000	65	352	130	704
5,000	68	400	135	800
6,000	70	441	139	882
8,000	73	509	146	1018
10,000	75	565	150	1129
15,000	80	668	159	1335
20,000	83	745	165	1490

Table 3. Minimum separation at pyrotechnic manufacturing plants

Pyrotechnics net weight, lb	Separation, ft			
	Class 1 & 2	Class 3 & 4 (barricaded)	Class 1 & 2	Class 3 & 4 (barricaded)
100	30	30	37	57
200	30	35	37	69
400	30	44	37	85
600	30	51	37	97
800	30	56	37	105
1,000	30	60	37	112
2,000	30	76	37	172
3,000	35	87	48	222
4,000	38	95	60	264
5,000	42	103	67	300
6,000	45	109	72	331
8,000	50	120	78	382
10,000	54	129	82	423

Chapter XVI

REFERENCES

1. Settles, J.E., *Deficiencies in the Testing and Classification of Dangerous Materials,* Annals of the New York Academy of Sciences, October 28, 1968; Vol. 152, Art. 1, p. 199.
2. Marshall, A., *Explosives,* J. and A. Churchill, London, 1917-32; Vols I and II.
3. *Guide to the Explosives Act,* 1875, Her Majesty's Stationery Office, London, 1962.
4. *DOD Ammunition and Explosives Safety Standards,* March 1976, DOD 5154. 45, Office of the Assistant Secretary of Defense for Installations and Logistics, Superintendent of Documents, U.S. Government Printing Office, Washington, D.C., No. 1008-007-02730-1.
5. Robinson, C.S., *Explosions, Their Anatomy and Destructiveness,* McGraw-Hill, New York, 1944.

GENERAL BIBLIOGRAPHY

1. Galway, A.K., *Chemistry of Solids,* Chapman and Hall, London, 1967 (distributed in U.S. by Barnes & Noble).
2. Moore, W.J., *Seven Solid States: An Introduction to the Chemistry and Physics of Solids,* W.A. Benjamin, Reading, Mass., 1967.
3. Mott, N.F. and Jones, H., *The Theory of the Properties of Metals and Alloys,* Dover, New York, 1936.
4. Hannay, N.B., *Solid State Chemistry,* Prentice-Hall, Englewood Cliffs, N.J., 1967.
5. Goldsmid, H.J., *Thermal Properties of Solids,* Dover, New York, 1965.
6. Rice, F.O. and Teller, E., *The Structure of Matter,* Wiley, New York, 1949.
7. Hume-Rothery, W., *Electrons, Atoms, Metals and Alloys,* 3rd ed., Dover, New York, 1963.
8. Hedvall, J.A., *Solid State Chemistry, Whence, Where and Whither,* Elsevier, London, 1966.
9. Mitchell, J.W., DeVries, R.C., Roberts, R.W., and Cannon, P., Eds., *Proceedings of the 6th International Symposium on the Reactivity of Solids* 1968, Wiley-Interscience, New York, 1969.
10. Anderson, J.F., Roberts, M.W., and Stone, F.S., Eds. *Proceedings of the 7th International Symposium on the Reactivity of Solids,* Chapman and Hall, London, 1972.
11. Mandelcorn, L., Ed., *Nonstoichiometric Solids,* Academic Press, New York, 1964.
12. Gregg, S.J., *The Surface Chemistry of Solids,* 2nd ed., Chapman and Hall, London, 1965.
13. Garner, W.E., Ed., *Chemistry of the Solid State,* Butterworth, London, 1955 (available from University Microfilms, Ann Arbor, Mich.).
14. Desch, C.H., *Chemistry of Solids,* Cornell University Press, Ithaca, N.Y., 1934.
15. Fyfe, W.S., Ed., *Geochemistry of Solids: An Introduction,* McGraw-Hill, New York, 1964.
16. Kubaschewski, O. and Catterall, J.A., *Thermochemical Data of Alloys,* Pergamon Press, London, 1956.
17. Gray, T.J. et al, *The Defect Solid State,* Interscience, New York, 1957.
18. Greenwood, N.N., *Ionic Crystals, Lattice Defects and Nonstoichiometry,* Chemical Publishing Co., New York, 1970.
19. Hauffe, K., *Reaktionen in und an festen stoffen,* Springer Verlag, Berlin, 1955; Vols. I and II. (Trans., "Reactions in and on Solids," U.S. Atomic Energy Commission, Division of Technical Information, Oak Ridge, Tenn., 1955.)
20. Ubbelohde, P.R., *Melting and Crystal Structure,* Clarendon Press, Oxford, 1955.
21. Budnikov, P.P. and Giustling, A.M., *Solid State Chemistry* (Engl. trans.), Gordon and Breach, New York, 1968.
22. Cackett, J.C., *Monograph on Pyrotechnic Compositions,* Royal Armament Research and Development Establishment, Fort Halstead, Seven Oaks, Kent, England, 1965 (RESTRICTED).
23. *Engineering Design Handbook, Military Pyrotechnic Series,* Part I, "Theory and Application," AMCP 706-185, U.S. Army Materiel Command, April 1967.

24. *Engineering Design Handbook,* "Explosive Trains," AMCP 706-179, U.S. Army Materiel Command, March 1965.

25. Shidlovskiy, A.A., *Foundations of Pyrotechnics,* Report FTD-II-63-758 (trans. DDC AD 602 687), Air Force Systems Command, Wright-Patterson AFB, Ohio, 1964.

26. Davis, T.L., *The Chemistry of Powders and Explosives,* Wiley, New York, 1941.

27. Taylor, J., *Solid Propellant and Exothermic Compositions,* George Newnes, London, 1959.

28. *DOD Contractors' Safety Manual for Ammunition, Explosives and Related Dangerous Material,* DOD 4145.26M, U.S. Department of Defense, October 1968 (available from Superintendent of Documents, U.S. Government Printing Office).

29. *Interstate Commerce Commission Regulations for Transportation of Explosives,* Agent T.C. George's Tariff No. 19, 63 Vesey St., New York, N.Y. 10007.

30. *Engineering Design Handbook,* "Properties of Explosives of Military Interest," AMCP 706-177, AD-814 964, U.S. Army Materiel Command, August 1963.

31. Johnson, D.M., *Proposed Kinetics and Mechanics of Illuminant Flares; Maximizing Efficiency,* RDTR No. 32, U.S. Naval Ammunition Depot, Crane, Ind., Jan. 1966.

32. Gibson, J.R. and Weber, J.D., *Handbook of Selected Properties of Air and Water Reactive Materials,* RDTR No. 144, U.S. Naval Ammunition Depot, Crane, Ind., March 1969.

33. Ripley, W., *The Effects of Selected Contaminants on the Hygroscopicity of Sodium Nitrate,* RDTR No. 140, U.S. Naval Ammunition Depot, Crane, Ind., March 1969.

34. Ripley, W., *Differential Thermal Analysis Thermograms of Sodium Nitrate Doped with Selected Contaminants,* RDTR No. 143, U.S. Naval Ammunition Depot, Crane, Ind., May 1969.

35. McLain, J.H. and McClure, M.D., *Effects of Phase Change in Solid-Solid Reactions, Final Report,* Grant DA-AMC-18-035-77(A), Chemical Research and Development Laboratories, Edgewood Arsenal, Md., April 1968.

36. McLain, J.H. and McClure, M.D., *Effects of Phase Change in Solid-Solid Reactions, Annual Report,* Grant DA-AMC-18-035-77(A), Chemical Research and Development Laboratories, Edgewood Arsenal, Md., November 1966.

37. McLain, J.H. and Lewis, D.V., *Effects of Phase Change in Solid-Solid Reactions, Annual Report,* Grant DA-AMC-18-035-77(A), Task 1C014501B71A02, Chemical Research and Development Laboratories, Edgewood Arsenal, Md., October 1965.

38. Taylor, J., *Detonation in Condensed Explosives,* Oxford University Press, London, 1952.

39. Zeldovitch, I.B. and Kompaneets, A.S., *Theory of Detonation,* Academic Press, New York, 1960.

40. Bowden, F.P. and Yoffe, A.D., *Initiation and Growth of Explosion in Liquid and Solids,* Cambridge University Press, Cambridge, England, 1952.

41. Ellern, H., *Military and Civilian Pyrotechnics,* Chemical Publishing Co., New York, 1968.

42. Wendlandt, W.W., *Thermal Methods of Analysis,* Interscience, New York, 1964.

43. Watkins, T.F., Cackett, J.C., and Hall, R.G., *Chemical Warfare, Pyrotechnics and the Fireworks Industry,* Pergamon Press, New York, 1968.

44. Lancaster, R., Shimizu, T., Butler, R.E.A., and Hall, R.G., *Fireworks Principles and Practice,* Chemical Publishing Co., New York, 1972.

45. Weingart, G.W., *Pyrotechnics,* 2nd ed., Chemical Publishing Co., New York, 1947.

46. *Ordnance Explosive Train Designers Handbook,* NOLR 1111, Naval Ordnance Laboratory, Washington, D.C., 1952.

47. *Advances in Chemistry Series 88,* "Propellants Manufacture, Hazards and Testing," American Chemical Society, Washington, D.C., 1969.

48. Van Gelder, A.P. and Schlatter, H., *History of the Explosives Industry in America,* Columbia University Press, New York, 1927.

49. *Guide to the Explosives Act 1875,* Her Majesty's Stationery Office, London, 1962.

50. Ohart, T.C., *Elements of Ammunition,* Wiley, New York, 1946.

51. *Proceedings 5th International Seminar,* Denver Research Institute, University of Denver, Denver, Col., 1976.

52. *Pyrotechnik Grundlagen, Technologie und Anwendung,* Institute fur Chemie der Treib- und Explosivstoffe, Karlesruhe, W. Germany, 1975.

53. *Proceedings of 1st Pyrotechnic Seminar,* U.S. Naval Ammunition Depot, Crane, Ind., 1968.

54. Hansson, J., *Pyroteknikdagen 1969, 1971, 1973, 1975, and 1977,* Sectionen for Detonik och Forbranning, Sundbyberg, Sweden.

55. Hansson, J., *Chemical Problems Connected with the Stability of Explosives, 1, 2, 3, and 4,* Sectionen for Detonik och Forbranning, Sundyberg, Sweden, 1970, 1972, 1974, and 1976.

56. *Pyrochem International,* University of Surrey, 1975; sponsored by the Royal Armament Research and Development Establishment, Langhurst, Horsham, Sussex, England.

57. Robinson, C.S., *Explosions, Their Anatomy and Destructiveness,* McGraw-Hill, New York and London, 1944.

AUTHOR INDEX

SUBJECT INDEX